REVIEWS IN ENGINEERING GEOLOGY
VOLUME IX

LANDSLIDES/LANDSLIDE MITIGATION

Edited by

JAMES E. SLOSSON
Slosson and Associates
15500 Erwin Street, Suite 1123
Van Nuys, California 91411

ARTHUR G. KEENE
2601 E. Victoria Street, #308
Rancho Dominguez, California 90220

and

JEFFREY A. JOHNSON
Jeffrey A. Johnson, Inc.
12818 Stebick Court
San Diego, California 92130

The Geological Society of America
3300 Penrose Place, P.O. Box 9140
Boulder, Colorado 80301
1992

Published by The Geological Society of America, Inc.
3300 Penrose Place, P.O. Box 9140, Boulder, Colorado 80301

Printed in U.S.A.

Library of Congress Cataloging-in-Publication Data
Landslides/landslide mitigation / edited by James E. Slosson, Arthur
    G. Keene, and Jeffrey A. Johnson.
        p.   cm. — (Reviews in engineering geology ; v. 9)
        Includes bibliographical references and index.
        ISBN 0-8137-4109-2
        1. Landslides.   2. Slopes (Soil mechanics)   I. Slosson, James E.,
    1923–   . II. Keene, Arthur G.   III. Johnson, Jeffrey A., 1956–
    IV. Series.
    TA710.2.L36   1992
    624.1'51—dc20   92-34189
                                                              CIP

10   9   8   7   6   5   4   3   2   1

Contents

PART I

1. **Compound Landslides: Nature and Hazard Potential of Secondary Landslides Within Host Landslides** 1
Vincent S. Cronin

2. **Surficial Slope Failures in Southern California Hillside Residential Areas: Lessons from the 1978 and 1980 Rainstorms** 11
P. M. Merifield

3. **The Concept of 'Reasonable Care' on Unstable Hillsides** 23
Robert B. Olshansky and J. David Rogers

4. **Differentiation Between Normal Residence Performance and Landslide-Related Distress in the Evaluation and Treatment of Slope Instability in Southern California** 29
Hugh S. Robertson and Robert A. Hollingsworth

PART II

5. **The Mameyes, Puerto Rico, Landslide Disaster of October 7, 1985** 37
Randall W. Jibson

6. **Landslide Failure at 20510 Callon Drive, Topanga, California, March 1978** 55
Arthur G. Keene

7. **Landslide Mitigation Using Horizontal Drains, Pacific Palisades Area, Los Angeles, California** 63
James P. Krohn

8. **Ground Water in the Abalone Cove Landslide, Palos Verdes Peninsula, Southern California** 69
Kathleen A. Proffer

Contents

9. Thistle Landslide: Was Mitigation Possible? 83
James E. Slosson, Delmar D. Yoakum, and Gerard Shuirman

10. Recent Developments in Landslide Mitigation Techniques 95
J. David Rogers

Index 119

Geological Society of America
Reviews in Engineering Geology, Volume IX
1992

Chapter 1

Compound landslides: Nature and hazard potential of secondary landslides within host landslides

Vincent S. Cronin
Department of Geosciences, University of Wisconsin-Milwaukee, Wisconsin 53201

ABSTRACT

Large host landslides commonly encompass smaller, secondary landslides; hence the term "compound landslide." Secondary landslides differ significantly from their host landslide in that secondary slides (1) have smaller volume; (2) often have greater surface exposure; (3) are more readily saturated by water infiltration; (4) require a smaller driving force to initiate movement; (5) have greater frequency of movement; and (6) their capacity for movement can be either independent of the host and other adjacent secondary landslides, or induced by adjacent landslides. Multilevel flow systems (perched water tables) commonly form within compound landslides due to the relatively low permeability of slip-surface gouge, which may slow recharge from the overlying secondary landslides to the host landslide. Movement-inducing pore-fluid pressures can often be reached more rapidly in secondary landslides. Controlled sources of water, for example, from irrigation and septic waste-water injection systems, can supplement vastly natural recharge from rainfall, artificially maintaining saturation in near-surface secondary landslides.

The progressive movement of a host landslide can generate a family of precursive failure surfaces in the landslide's interior that can coalesce to form secondary landslides. Evolution of local topography contributes to the morphology and slip direction of secondary landslides to the extent that stress trajectories within a host landslide are perturbed by changes in the shape of the ground surface; for example, increased slope gradient along a landslide's toe is a common cause of secondary landsliding. The non-plane strain nature of compound landslides, exemplified by the complex interactions between host and secondary landslides, often precludes the meaningful application of general, plane strain, mechanical models in assessing the hazard potential of a specific compound landslide. Rote stability analyses of compound landslides based upon assumed homogeneous, isotropic, linear-elastic behavior throughout the slide prism fail to consider the intrinsically more unstable (and thus more hazardous) secondary landslides.

Geologists involved in landslide exploration must be aware of the characteristics of compound landsliding; those involved in mitigation must consider the hydrologic and dynamic implications of secondary landsliding in order to conduct the requisite field investigations and make appropriate design recommendations, which must be individually suited to each compound landslide.

INTRODUCTION

A given landslide can be a very extensive feature that, when considered in its entirety, may seem to be stable under conditions that can reasonably be expected to occur. Insufficient attention is often paid to the components of a landslide that may pose particular hazards should they become active independent of the main landslide mass. A common example is a debris flow that origi-

Cronin, V. S., 1992, Compound landslides: Nature and hazard potential of secondary landslides within host landslides, *in* Slosson, J. E., Keene, A. G., and Johnson, J. A., eds., Landslides/Landslide Mitigation: Boulder, Colorado, Geological Society of America Reviews in Engineering Geology, v. IX.

nates within a preexisting landslide deposit—the active debris flow may be volumetrically insignificant relative to the parent landslide, however, the debris flow can be of great significance to the structures or lives that it affects. It is irrelevant that a geologist may have determined the landslide mass as a whole to be stable; a landslide complex is not stable unless all of its significant elements are stable.

This chapter represents a preliminary description of compound landslides. The characterization of a landslide as "compound" is rather artificial, because landslide prisms probably all undergo internal deformation during transport, leading to the segmentation of an original continuous medium into linked, discontinuous landslide arrays. The purpose of this chapter is to provide a simple conceptual model of compound landsliding that is intended to help engineering geologists to recognize compound landslides in the field, gain a basic understanding of the genesis and structure of compound landslides, and appreciate the hazard potential posed by subsidiary elements of landslide complexes.

General nature of compound landslides

A compound landslide is a landslide that has calved or become segmented into smaller, secondary landslides (Fig. 1). The landslide mass from which a secondary landslide is derived is termed a host landslide. The unstable mass in its entirety is the compound landslide, a mechanically and hydrologically discontinuous entity that generally undergoes inhomogeneous nonplane strain during periods of instability.

Compound landslides are ubiquitous in landslide-prone areas, and are observed throughout the hillside areas of coastal southern California. California continues to be a structurally dynamic area in which rock materials as diverse as Precambrian anorthosites and Quaternary marine mudstones are actively being uplifted, and subsequently degraded by mass wasting. Notable examples of compound landslides in southern California include the following: the Bluebird Canyon landslide at Laguna Beach; the San Juan Creek landslide complex in San Juan Capistrano; the Portuguese Bend and Abalone Cove landslides on the Palos Verdes Peninsula; the Big Rock Mesa, Rambla Pacifico, and Carbon Canyon landslides at Malibu; and the several landslide complexes near Grapevine along U.S. Interstate Highway 5, on the northern edge of the Transverse Ranges.

Secondary landslides have a smaller volume than their host landslides, so they require a smaller driving force to initiate movement. Secondary landslides often have a greater ratio of surface exposure to volume. As a consequence, secondary landslides may be more readily saturated with water, either through surface infiltration or by injection from some other source, as from septic systems or leaky pipes. Their smaller volume and relative ease of attaining saturation explain why secondary landslides tend to move more frequently than their hosts. Furthermore, secondary landslides often move farther and with a greater velocity during their periods of activity than their larger host landslide. In summary, secondary landslides present a large and often-unrecognized hazard potential.

STRUCTURAL CONSIDERATIONS

Secondary landslides influenced by surface topography

The shape and slip direction of secondary landslides are generally determined by local ground-water conditions, surface morphology, the material properties of the bedrock, and the presence, density, and orientation of structural flaws within the host landslide. The surface morphology of a slope changes as a host landslide moves. Local increases in slope gradient within the host landslide often lead to the development of secondary landslides and surficial debris flows. (Although debris-flow genesis is beyond the scope of this chapter, note that the deformation of a landslide mass upon transport may contribute to the generation of mechanically disaggregated material on the landslide surface, which can then be easily saturated and mobilized during intense rainstorms.) Increases in slope gradient within a landslide occur along the landslide's toe, along headscarps and grabens, and adjacent to drainages that may be deeply incised into the landslide mass. Many examples of secondary slope failure due to the development of pronounced drainage channels within transport-weakened landslide material can be seen in the Big Rock Mesa compound landslide at Malibu and in the large compound landslides near Grapevine.

Secondary landslides related to transport deformation of the host landslide

The movement of a host landslide often leads to the development of failure surfaces within the host that may coalesce to form secondary landslides. Stability analyses of slopes and land-

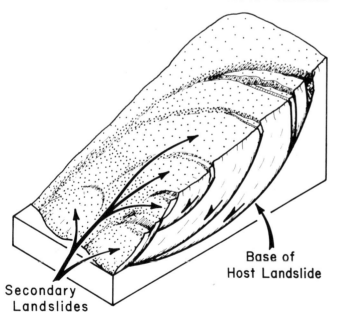

Figure 1. Block diagram of a compound landslide, showing a variety of secondary landslides.

Base of Host Landslide

Secondary Landslides

slides are commonly based on the assumption that the subject volume represents an intact, mechanically continuous landslide prism that is at rest on a planar, spherical, or cylindrical surface in accordance with the law of static friction. In addition to permitting the use of the relatively simple concepts of statics, this approach allows the analyst to neglect the effects of internal deformation within the landslide prism, because a landslide can move as a rigid body along a planr, spherical, or cylindrical slip surface without losing continuity along the slip surface. Landslides that deform during transport evolve into a series of discrete elements whenever significant movement occurs on internal deformation surfaces. Mechanical continuity in a deforming medium is, to some extent, dependent on the scale of interest for a given problem. Engineering geologists are primarily interested in discontinuities whose effects are sufficiently large to pose a hazard to human safety and to the integrity of roads, buildings, and other structures. Clearly, secondary landslides satisfy this criterion as significant discontinuities within large landslides.

Let us imagine a simple, isotropic, homogeneous linear-elastic landslide on a perfectly planar, spherical, or cylindrical slip surface—the "textbook" landslide (Fig. 2). First-order stability analyses often use the empirical, static friction relation of Mohr-Coulomb as a failure criterion. This relation indicates that a plane of maximum resolved shear stress exists within a medium at a material-dependent angle that is commonly 30° from the maximum compressive stress axis. Principal stress axes are mapped either parallel or perpendicular to a free surface (i.e., a surface along which there is no resolved shear stress).

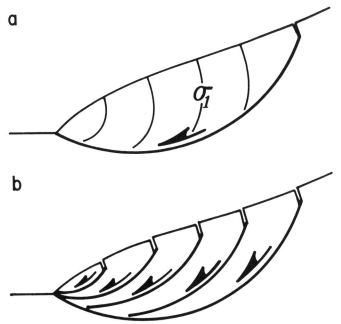

Figure 2. Stress state in a hypothetical, homogeneous, isotropic, linear-elastic landslide prism. a: Some maximum principal compressive stress (σ_1) trajectories, which are perpendicular to the free ground surface along the top of the landslide. b: Some possible normal fault surfaces within the landslide prism, based on the stress state depicted in Figure 2a.

The hypothetical, maximum compressive stress trajectories illustrated in Figure 2a are perpendicular to the free surface constituted by the ground, honoring the common field observation of extension fracture oriented perpendicular to the ground. At the base of the landslide prism, the maximum compressive stress trajectories are mapped at an angle of ~30° from the basal shear surface. A sampling of the corresponding family of potential shear trajectories is shown in Figure 2b. Given sufficient shear stress, one or more of these shear surfaces may become active due to drag along the basal slip surface as the landslide moves. Propagation of drag-related fractures may result in the segmentation of the landslide prism, causing it to evolve into a compound landslide.

Cloos (1968) simulated the development of drag-related faults in a series of clay model experiments investigating normal faults. Evidence of drag faulting within traveling blocks above listric normal faults has been gathered from well data (e.g., Berg and others, 1979), as well as from seismic reflection profiling (e.g., Wintershall, *in* Wernicke and Burchfiel, 1982, Fig. 15).

If the assumption of a perfectly planar, spherical, or cylindrical slip surface is relaxed to conform more closely with naturally occurring conditions, it is clear that a landslide prism will be deformed as it moves over bumps or asperities in its slip surface (Fig. 3). An area along which the curvature of a landslide's slip surface changes significantly will be a region of stress concentration that may be sufficient to cause fracturing or faulting in an overriding volume of rock. A common example of deformation of a landslide as it passes over a stress concentrator is provided along the toe of a typical rotational landslide. The region where the arcuate slip surface emerges at the toe of a landslide is a region of stress concentration in which the landslide toe is deformed as it moves over the convex stress concentrator (cf. Figs. 3b and 4).

Erosion may remove the slide material almost as fast as it is deposited beyond the stress concentrator, resulting in the progressive development of a scarp above the host landslide's toe. This scarp will grow rapidly during the early history of the landslide, leading to additional slope failures along the scarp. Wave erosion of coastal landslides can contribute to the creation of bluffs within unstable landslide material, as seen at the base of the Portuguese Bend landslide (Fig. 4) and at Big Rock Mesa.

A landslide deforms as it passes over an irregular slip surface in much the same way that a thrust sheet deforms as it moves over a ramp (e.g., Berger and Johnson, 1980), or as a glacier deforms as it slides along an irregular base (e.g., Budd, 1970, 1971). Pronounced extensional joints (crevasses) develop in the glacier's brittle upper layer as the glacier passes over bumps in the basal slip surface (Fig. 5). In zones of shortening, pressure ridges and shallow thrust faults develop on the glacier's surface, accompanied by pressure solution and recrystallization of the ice in areas of particularly high stress. Despite their different material properties, there is a marked morphological similarity between the hummocky topography on the surface of some landslides and that of glaciers that flow over irregular surfaces (cf. Figs. 3, 4, 5, and 6).

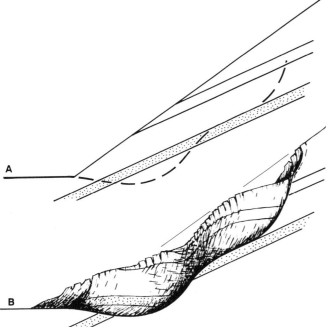

Figure 3. Deformation of a landslide as it moves over an irregular slip surface. A: Slope and bedrock configuration prior to failure. Note the initial continuity and orientation of the stippled marker bed, and the linear profile of the slope. B: Schematic cross-section of the slope after a moderate amount of slip. Rigid-body rotation has occurred above the concave-upward segments of the slip surface (note passive markers), and ductile-cataclastic deformation typifies the regions of stress concentration above the significant bumps in the basal fault. Extension fractures along the ground surface define blocks that become rotated and translated through movement on deeper shear surfaces. The surface morphology becomes hummocky as a result of landslide movement over an irregular base.

Figure 4. View of the imbricate slope failures along the toe of the Portuguese Bend landslide, California, looking northeast from Inspiration Point. The cross-section shows the relation of these toe failures to the area where the slip surface changes shape as it reaches the ground surface. (Cross-section is modified from Ehlig, 1986, sec. A-A'). PVDS is Palôs Verdes Drive South.

It generally requires less work to move along existing, favorably oriented planes of weakness than to break unfractured rock. Strain is localized along a given zone of relative weakness within a landslide for as long as that weak zone is the deformation path of least resistance. The shape of an internal failure surface may change through time as the landslide prism continues to deform. As deformation surfaces strain harden, perhaps due to rotation of the surfaces into orientations that cause them to lock rather than to slide, displacement is transferred to newly activated deformation surfaces along which it takes less work to continue movement.

Internal deformation within a compound landslide should not be assumed to be distributed in a homogeneous manner throughout the landslide prism. Rafts of relatively undeformed material are often observed within active landslides. Similar rafts have been described within glacially deformed till deposits (Banham, 1975). Large, relatively undeformed blocks within a deformed matrix are term "olistoliths" in the context of submarine

Figure 5. Deformation in a glacier as it passes over an irregular slip surface. Extensional fractures (crevasses) form above significant bumps in the slip surface.

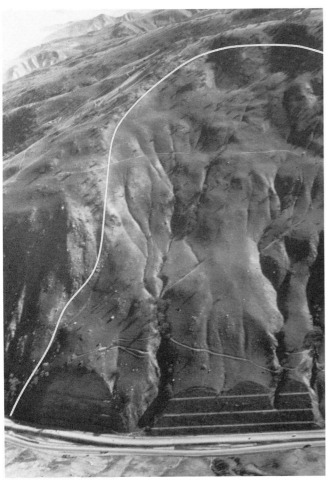

Figure 6. A portion of the compound landslide complex along Interstate Highway 5 at Grapevine, California. The most obvious large landslide is outlined in white, although all of the slope areas in the photograph are probably involved in landsliding. Note the hummocky topography and the steep cut slopes along the toe of the landslide. Total relief of this landslide is ~750 m. Debris flows originating within landslides in this area have already cost one life and caused extensive property damage. Photo by J. E. Slosson.

Figure 7. The Rambla Pacifico landslide in Las Flores Canyon at Malibu, California. Several of the major secondary landslides that cross Rambla Pacifico Road are outlined in white. Remnants of the destroyed roadway and houses can be seen within the landslide mass. Total relief of this landslide is ~120 m.

gravity tectonics. The reservoirs of the Rosita and South Hallettsville gas fields are contained within the core of large olistoliths that remained largely intact during their downslope movement (Berg, 1981). Excellent examples of strain localization within a large landslide can be seen along the toe scarp of the Big Rock Mesa landslide at Malibu, where enormous blocks of largely undeformed sandstone and conglomerate are surrounded by zones of pervasively deformed material.

The mere presence of undeformed material within a volume that is suspected of being a landslide prism does not represent conclusive evidence that the suspicious slope area is not involved in landsliding. The danger of identifying relatively undeformed rock material as in-place bedrock has been vividly demonstrated

in the history of the Rambla Pacifico landslide at Malibu (Fig. 7). A macroscopically undeformed sandstone bed was observed within the perimeter of a suspected landslide prior to the development of a series of lots along Rambla Pacifico Road. It was argued that the presence of the apparently intact sandstone bed constituted conclusive evidence that the hillside was stable, in spite of clear geomorphic indicators to the contrary. Today, the Rambla Pacifico landslide could serve well as the type example of a compound landslide; in retrospect, several of the currently active secondary landslides were identifiable on predevelopment aerial photographs. Eight homes and a vital roadway have been destroyed by movement of this large compound landslide since 1978 (Sowma, 1986).

Movement of one landslide may induce the movement of other landslides, resulting in a chain of instability. The movement of a landslide may cause the rapid loading of a subjacent landslide, whch may subsequently move due to the increase in weight and fluid pressure (Fig. 8). Alternately, the movement of a landslide may result in the removal of support from a superjacent landslide, leading to a critical decrease in the higher landslide's resistance to movement. The movement of the second landslide may induce the movement of a third landslide, and so on. Standard methods of stability analysis may indicate gross stability for landslides located within specific property lines; however, the responsible geologist must also recognize the dangers posed by off-site conditions that may initiate a chain of instability due to either sequential loading or the removal of support.

Summary

Compound landslides are mechanically discontinuous. The movement of a host landslide leads to the development of failure

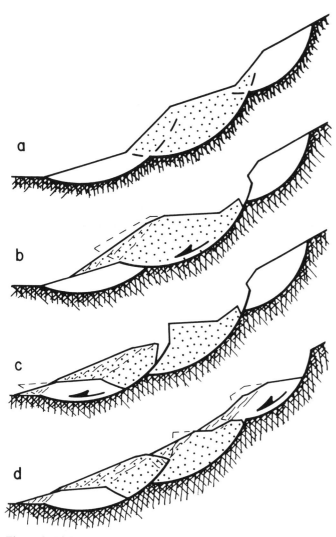

Figure 8. Linkage among adjacent landslides to produce a chain of instability. a: The original slope configuration. b: The middle (stippled) landslide moves, rapidly loading the lower slide prism and removing support from the upper slide prism. c: The lower landslide then becomes active due to the increase in shear stress, followed by (d) movement of the unsupported upper slide mass.

surfaces that may coalesce to form secondary landslides. Secondary landslides generally invalidate the plane-strain assumption used in many of the standard mechanical analyses of landslide stability. Typical stability analyses that would tacitly consider a compound landslide to be a mechanically continuous, linear-elastic medium do not resolve the stability of included secondary landslides. As a result, rote stability analyses may overestimate the stability of a given compound landslide. The possible error is particularly significant because it concerns the stability of the most potentially hazardous elements of the landslide complex: the secondary landslides.

HYDROGEOLOGIC CONSIDERATIONS

The structural geology of compound landslides is inextricably linked to their hydrology. In addition to the Terzaghi effect, whereby fluid pressure decreases the effective normal stress on a shear surface (Terzaghi, 1950), surface and ground water play a crucial role in the evolution of secondary landslides through such processes as dissolution of grains or intergranular cement, mechanical erosion through piping, and pressurized crack growth.

Ground-water recharge

High levels of ground water can lead to slope failure in natural areas where the ground-water reservoir is recharged solely by infiltration of rain water. The relation between rainfall and slope failure has been amply documented in the literature (e.g., Briggs and others, 1975; Campbell, 1975; Fleming and Taylor, 1980; Fleming and others, 1979; Krohn and Slosson, 1976; Nilson and Brabb, 1972; Nilson and others, 1976; Nilson and Turner, 1975; Radbruch-Hall and others, 1982; Schuster and Krizek, 1978; Slosson and Krohn, 1979, 1982). Rainfall is known to have induced major slope failures in southern California in 1952, 1958, 1962, 1969, 1973, 1978, and 1980.

Landslides are commonly induced by rainfall in areas of suitable topography and geology in the Santa Monica Mountains of southern California when the total seasonal (antecedent) rainfall reaches at least ~25.5 cm (10 in), and when the local rainfall intensity exceeds ~0.5 cm (0.20 in) per hour (Campbell, 1975). Slosson and Krohn (1982) modified this empirical model by suggesting that the conditions for rain-induced slope failure have been reached when the antecedent rainfall is above average and "at least five or more days of high-intensity rainfall [occur] during which at least ~18 cm (7 in) of rainfall" is recorded. For comparison, the maximum rainfall yet recorded in southern California is ~84 cm (33 in) in 1884, whereas the average rainfall at Malibu is roughly 36–51 cm (15 to 20 in) per year.

Natural sources of ground-water recharge are augmented in urbanized areas by septic waste-water injection, irrigation, leaky pipes, and improper drainage devices. The artificial introduction of water into hillside areas has the effect of decreasing the volume of rainwater necessary to trigger slope failures. The subsurface disposal of septic waste water is generally the most significant ground-water contribution by people. Irrigation may add the equivalent ~51 cm (20 in) of rainfall annually to a residential area. Leaky pipes and cracked drainage devices are generally aftereffects of landslide movement, and serve to aggravate an existing problem. Runoff volumes are increased by urbanization, with the introduction of impermeable cover in the form of roofs and paved roadways. To the extent that the increased runoff is not collected by a drainage system and conducted away from slope areas with suitable flood-control devices, the additional water can contribute to mudflows, flooding, and the further saturation of existing or potential landslide masses.

Rainfall can trigger slope failures under certain commonly experienced conditions. Similarly, the injection of septic waste water directly into the subsurface can also lead to slope failure, both as the sole source of ground-water recharge and in concert with natural rainfall. A simple calculation illustrates this point. Let us assume the following conditions: 380 l (100 gal) of septic discharge per person each day; a constant soil-infiltration rate of 5%; and 36–51 cm (15–20 in) of rainfall annually in a hypothetical location. The septic discharge of a typical two-person house compares with the water that falls as rainfall on a bare quarter-acre lot and successfully migrates into the ground-water supply as follows.

Septic discharge = (2 persons) × (380 l/person day) × (365.25 days/year)
Septic discharge = 277,590 l or ~73,050 gal per year.

Infiltration from rainfall = (0.51 m/year) × (~4,047 m²/acre) ×
  0.25 acre × (1,000 l/m³) × 0.05
Infiltration from rainfall = ~25,800 l or ~6,800 gal per year.

At 51 cm (20 in) of rainfall per year, septic discharge is more than *10 times* the infiltration of rainwater; at 36 cm (15 in) of annual rainfall, the contribution from septic systems to the ground-water reservoir is almost *15 times* more significant than that of rainfall.

The contribution from septic systems to ground-water recharge can exceed greatly that of rainfall in some urbanized areas. The above example indicates that it would take roughly 500 cm (200 in) of rain on a bare quarter-acre lot to equal the amount of water that reaches the ground-water reservoir in an average year from a septic system beneath a typical two-person house—10 to 15 times the normal precipitation along the landslide-prone Malibu region. This is a very conservative estimate, because *all* of the septic water goes directly into the subsurface, whereas about two-thirds of the rainwater leaves the system via evapotranspiration and most of the remaining third is lost as runoff. The presence of septic systems in hillside areas can lead to primary, as well as to secondary, landslides.

Development of fracture permeability, flow barriers, and flow paths within landslides

The introduction of ground water into the conceptual model leads to the suggestion of possible hydrologic contributions to slip-surface formation. Water acts chemically to weaken the rock through dissolution of grains and cement, as well as by bonding to the interlayers of expandable hydrophylic clay minerals. Dissolution of cement in a grain-supported aggregate weakens the rock by shifting stress concentrations from grain interiors to grain boundaries (Gallagher and others, 1974).

Fractures within landslides probably fill with moving fluid as soon as they form, becoming local conduits for ground-water flow. The localization of fluid flow along fault planes has been noted in a well-delimited setting involving a listric normal fault system at the McAllen Ranch gas field of southern Texas (Berg and Habeck, 1982). In this example, the traveling block above the master normal fault is deformed by intrablock faulting that involves both pinnate drag faults dipping in the same sense as the main normal fault and antithetic faults associated with a rollover structure. Pressure data acquired from a number of gas wells show that fluid pressure in excess of the normal hydrostatic pressure occurs in the interior of the traveling block, probably due to a combinationn of clay transformation and hydrocarbon generation. The distribution of fluid pressure within the traveling block suggests that hydrodynamic flow is occurring from the regions of anomalously high pressure to areas of lower or normal pressure. Berg and Habeck (1982) concluded that the faults that exist within the traveling block and along its base provide the conduits for hydrodynamic flow. Fracture permeability adjacent to faults can be sufficient to localize fluid flow *along* fault zones; however, grain comminution within a fault zone and consequent gouge development can significantly retard fluid flow *across* fault zones. The lower confining-pressure within a smaller subaerial landslide can be expected to provide more favorable conditions for the generation and preservation of fracture permeability adjacent to slip surfaces.

Localization of ground-water flow within a landslide often leads to mechanical erosion or piping along the flow path. Piping may, in turn, contribute to the maintenance of open fractures by introducing detrital grains as chockstones in the cracks, propping the fractures open. This process is the natural analog of the hydraulic-fracturing process commonly practiced in the petroleum industry, in which sand is pumped into a fractured reservoir to prevent the newly formed fractures from closing. Water also acts as a pressure-transmitting fluid that can dramatically accelerate microcrack growth (Kranz, 1983). Fault development through the coalescence of pressurized fractures across a water-weakened rock matrix may quickly follow initial microfracture development within the zone of maximum shear stress.

Ground-water flow paths within a simple, homogeneous landslide probably resemble those depicted in Figure 9A (Hubbert, 1940; Freeze and Cherry, 1979). If the movement of the simple landslide produces a permeable zone of fracture porosity adjacent to the slip surface, as it often does, then a two-layer flow system would develop within the landslide. The zone of higher hydraulic conductivity along the base of the landslide might act as a natural subdrain for the landslide prism (Fig. 9B). The evolution of a secondary landslide can be expected to result in a complex, multilayer flow system in which the secondary landslide's flow system may divert some of the ground-water flow away from the deeper elements of the compound landslide (Fig. 9C). The structural evolution of a compound landslide is related to the landslide's hydrological evolution into an inhomogeneous aquifer characterized by a multilevel flow system. This concept is

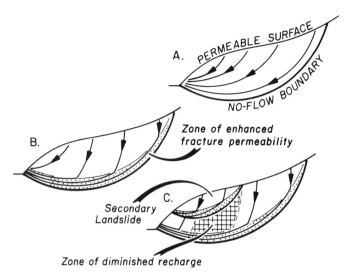

Figure 9. Hypothetical ground-water flow paths within compound land-slides. A: Flow paths within a homogeneous, isotropic landslide aquifer, with a no-flow boundary along the slip surface. B: Fracture permeability along the slip surface creates a multilevel flow system with consequent deflection of the flow lines. C: Secondary landsliding compounds the multilevel flow system. Superjacent zones of higher hydraulic conductivity may pirate recharge to lower elements of the compound landslide.

compatible with the common observance of perched water tables and springs located in unexpected places on large (compound) landslides.

The hydrologic complexity of a compound landslide may not be reflected in records of the long-term dry-season pumping response of dewatering wells. Behavior as a multilevel flow system may only be recognizable during episodes of increased recharge in the rainy season. It is no coincidence that this is also the most critical time relative to the instability of secondary landslides. Clearly, simple hydrologic models are not wholly adequate for the characterization of the ground-water state of a compound landslide.

CONCLUSIONS

Compound landslides present a challenging set of problems to geologists and engineers charged with landslide mitigation. Engineering geologists must learn to recognize, and predict the occurrence of compound landsliding, so that the unique mechanical problems posed by each compound landslide can be fully and safely resolved.

Some of the principal conclusions of this study are as follows.

1. Secondary landslides are generally the most hazardous elements of large landslides.

2. The origin of secondary landslides is related, in part, to the progressive development of deformation surfaces within large landslides as they move.

3. Local topography and bedrock geometry affects the shape and slip direction of secondary landslides.

4. The presence of ground water may lead to pressurized crack growth, dissolution of grains and cement, and mechanical erosion through piping, all of which facilitate the generation of failure surfaces along which primary and secondary landslides move.

5. Secondary landslides can become hydrologically isolated, leading to the development of multilevel flow systems that may be active principally during episodes of increased recharge during rainy seasons. This is also the most critical time relative to the saturation and consequent instability of secondary landslides. Dewatering projects should be designed to drain both host and secondary landslides.

6. When considering a compound landslide, it is inappropriate to apply hydrologic analyses that are based on the assumption that the landslide prism constitutes a single, homogeneous, isotropic, linear-elastic aquifer. Compound landslides are hydrologically discontinuous media.

7. Excessive irrigation and the subsurface injection of septic waste water in preexisting landslides can be critical to the activation or reactivation of secondary landslides. Human-controlled sources of water can vastly supplement natural recharge from rainfall, maintaining saturation in near-surface secondary landslides. Such artificial recharge must be discontinued if remedial dewatering efforts are to succeed.

8. Compound landslides are mechanically discontinuous media. Secondary landslides generally violate the plane strain assumption used in many mechanical analyses of landslide stability. Standard stability analyses of landslides generally do not account for secondary landslides, thereby underestimating the hazard potential of a compound landslide.

ACKNOWLEDGMENTS

This work would not have been possible without the guidance and financial assistance provided by J. E. Slosson and Slosson & Associates. C. C. Mathewson commented on early versions of abstracts related to this paper. Additional financial assistance was provided by the Department of Geology and the Center for Tectonophysics at Texas A&M University, and the Geosciences Department at the University of Wisconsin-Milwaukee.

REFERENCES CITED

Banham, P. H., 1975, Glaciotectonic structures: A general discussion with particular reference to the contorted drift of Norfolk, *in* Wright, A. E., and Moseley, F., eds., Ice ages: Modern and ancient: Journal of Geology, Special Issue 6, p. 69–94.

Berg, R. R., 1981, Deep-water reservoir sandstones of the Texas Gulf Coast: Gulf Coast Association of Geological Societies Transactions, v. 31, p. 31–38.

Berg, R. R., and Habeck, M. F., 1982, Abnormal pressures in the lower Vicksburg, McAllen Ranch field, south Texas: Gulf Coast Association of Geological Societies Transactions, v. 32, p. 247–253.

Berg, R. R., Marshall, W. D., and Shoemaker, P. W., 1979, Structural and depositional history, McAllen Ranch field, Hidalgo County, Texas: Gulf Coast Association of Geological Societies Transactions, v. 29, p. 24–28.

Berger, P., and Johnson, A. M., 1980, First-order analysis of deformation of a thrust sheet moving over a ramp: Tectonophysics, v. 70, p. T9–T24.

Briggs, R. P., Pomeroy, J. S., and Davies, W. E., 1975, Landsliding in Allegheny County, Pennsylvania: U.S. Geological Survey Circular 728, 18 p.

Budd, W. F., 1970, The longitudinal stress and strain-rate gradients in ice masses: Journal of Glaciology, v. 9, p. 19–27.

——— , 1971, Stress variations with ice flow over undulations: Journal of Glaciology, v. 10, p. 177–195.

Campbell, R. H., 1975, Soil slips, debris flows, and rainstorms in the Santa Monica Mountains and vicinity, southern California: U.S. Geological Survey Professional Paper 851, 51 p.

Cloos, E., 1968, Experimental analysis of Gulf Coast fracture patterns: American Association of Petroleum Geologists Bulletin, v. 52, p. 420–444.

Ehlig, P. L., 1986, The Portuguese Bend landslide: Its mechanics and a plan for its stabilization, *in* Ehlig, P. L., compiler, Landslides and landslide mitigation in southern California, Geological Society of America Cordilleran Section meeting guidebook: Los Angeles, California State University, p. 181–190.

Fleming, R. W., and Taylor, F. A., 1980, Estimating the costs of landslide damage in the United States: U.S. Geological Survey Circular 832, 21 p.

Fleming, R. W., Varnes, D. J., and Schuster, R. L., 1979, Landslide hazards and their reduction: Journal of American Institute of Planners, v. 45, no. 4, p. 428–439.

Freeze, R. A., and Cherry, J. A., 1979, Groundwater: Englewood Cliffs, New Jersey, Prentice-Hall, Inc., p. 168–189.

Gallagher, J. J., Friedman, M., Handin, J., and Sowers, G. M., 1974, Experimental studies relating to microfracture in sandstone: Tectonophysics, v. 21, p. 203–247.

Hubbert, M. K., 1940, The theory of groundwater motion: Journal of Geology, v. 48, p. 785–944.

Kranz, R. L., 1983, Microcracks in rocks: A review: Tectonophysics, v. 100, p. 449–480.

Krohn, J. P., and Slosson, J. E., 1976, Landslide potential in the United States: California Geology, October 1976, p. 224–231.

Nilson, T. H., and Brabb, E. E., 1972, Preliminary photointerpretation and dam-
age maps of landslide and other surficial deposits in northeastern San Jose, Santa Clara County, California: U.S. Geological Survey Miscellaneous Field Studies Map MF—361, 1 sheet, scale 1:24,000.

Nilson, T. H., and Turner, B. L., 1975, Influence of rainfall and ancient landslide deposits on recent landslides (1950–71) in urban areas of Contra Costa County, California: U.S. Geological Survey Bulletin 1388, 18 p.

Nilson, T. H., Taylor, F. A., and Brabb, E. E., 1976, Recent landslides in Alameda County, California (1940–71); An estimate of economic losses and correlation with slope, rainfall, and ancient landslide deposits: U.S. Geological Survey Bulletin 1398, 20 p.

Radbruch-Hall, D. H., Colton, R. B., Davies, W. E., Luccitta, I., Skipp, B. A., and Varnes, D. J., 1982, Landslide overview map of the conterminous United States: U.S. Geological Survey Professional Paper 1183, 25 p.

Schuster, R. L., and Krizek, R. J., eds., 1978, Landslides: Analysis and control: Washington, D.C., National Research Council, Transportation Research Board Special Report 176, 234 p.

Slosson, J. E., and Krohn, J. P., 1979, AEG building code review, mudflow/debris flow damage, February 1978 storm—Los Angeles area: California Geology, January 1979, p. 8–11.

——— , 1982, Southern California landslides of 1978 and 1980, *in* Jennings, P. C., and Brooks, N. H., eds., Storms, floods, and debris flows in southern California and Arizona 1978 and 1980: Washington, D.C., National Research Council, National Academy Press, p. 291–304.

Sowma, J. A., 1986, The Rambla Pacifico landslide, Malibu/La Costa area, California, *in* Ehlig, P. L., compiler, Landslides and landslide motion in southern California (Geological Society of America: Cordilleran Section meeting (Guidebook): Los Angeles, California State University, p. 181–190.

Terzaghi, K., 1950, Mechanism of landslides, *in* Application of engineering to geology (Berkey Volume): New York, Geological Society of America, p. 83–123.

Wernicke, B., and Burchfiel, B. C., 1982, Modes of extensional tectonics: Journal of Structural Geology, v. 4, p. 105–115.

MANUSCRIPT ACCEPTED BY THE SOCIETY FEBRUARY 21, 1992

Geological Society of America
Reviews in Engineering Geology, Volume IX
1992

Chapter 2

Surficial slope failures in southern California hillside residential areas: Lessons from the 1978 and 1980 rainstorms

P. M. Merifield*
Consulting Geologist, 3411 Wade Street, Los Angeles, California 90066

ABSTRACT

Widespread damage in hillside areas of southern California resulting from major rainstorms during 1978 and 1980 focused attention on risks to life and property from surficial slope failures, including debris slides, debris flows, and debris floods. Both artificial and natural slopes underwent damaging surficial failures; however, mountain and foothill areas below burned watersheds were affected by considerably more debris than unburned areas. Slopes vegetated with grasses or other ground cover lacking deep root systems were particularly susceptible to failure.

Preventive measures include stricter enforcement of existing grading codes (including the requirement for a continuous cover of deep-rooted vegetation), stability analyses of surficial failures, regional studies by state and local governments to identify hazardous areas, site-specific investigations by consultants when properties change hands, and increased efforts to educate the public about slope maintenance in order to mitigate slope failures.

INTRODUCTION

Debris slides, debris flows, and debris floods brought on by devastating rainstorms in 1978 and 1980 caused widespread damage to hillside residential properties in southern California. These events, as well as the 1982 rainstorms in northern California and the spring runoff in Utah in 1983, have increased awareness of the damage and loss of life that can result from surficial failures.

Natural slopes in southern California are commonly 1.5 horizontal to 1 vertical or steeper. The mantle of soil and colluvium, which is generally thinner than 1 m but accumulates to depths up to about 3 m in ravines, is therefore near its angle of repose.

Vegetation consists mostly of chaparral: shrubs that grow primarily in winter and form a nearly continuous canopy over the slopes. Sediment moves downslope principally during infrequent heavy rainstorms. The production of sediment increases enor-mously in burned areas when heavy rains follow brush fires within one to three years.

OVERVIEW OF 1978 AND 1980 STORMS

Precipitation, which occurs almost entirely in the winter months, averages about 38 cm (15 in; actual measurements are in inches) in the southern California coastal plains (but more than twice that in some mountain and foothill areas). Annual rainfalls of twice the average are not uncommon: since 1877, the Los Angeles Civic Center has recorded nine years of rainfall with seasonal totals between 66 and 96.5 cm (26 and 38 in).

In terms of intensity and severity of damage, the rainstorms culminating February 10 and March 4, 1978, and the mid-February storms of 1980 are prominent. Figure 1 shows the 1978 rainfall figures for Mt. Wilson in the San Gabriel Mountains, which commonly records the highest precipitation in southern California. The storm culminating on February 10 began five days earlier; on the night of February 9–10, more than 20 cm (8 in) of rain was recorded at some localities within a 24 hour period. One station at Crystal Lake in the San Gabriel Mountains recorded 33 cm (13 in) on February 10. Several southern California stations exceeded 100 year return periods of high-intensity

---

*Also Adjunct Professor, Department of Earth and Space Sciences, University of California, Los Angeles, California 90024.

Merifield, P. M., 1992, Surficial slope failures in southern California hillside residential areas: Lessons from the 1978 and 1980 rainstorms, *in* Slosson, J. E., Keene, A. G., and Johnson, J. A., eds., Landslides/Landslide Mitigation: Boulder, Colorado, Geological Society of America Reviews in Engineering Geology, v. IX.

P. M. Merifield

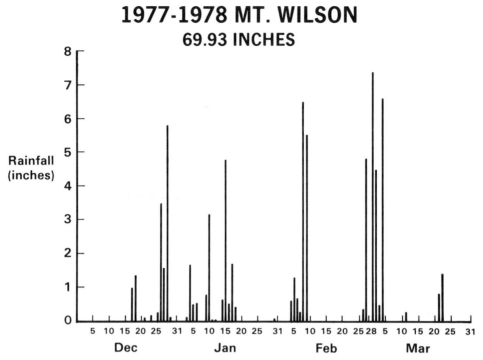

Figure 1. Daily rainfall, December–March, 1977–1978, Mt. Wilson station, NOAA climatological data.

rainfall (Pyke, 1982). However, these rainfall intensities for a given 24 hour period are not unique: on New Year's eve and New Year's day, 1933–34, Pasadena recorded 30.5 cm (12 in), and on January 25, 1969, more than 51 cm (20 in) of rain was recorded at some stations in the San Gabriel Mountains. The highest rainfall recorded in southern California for a single 24 hour period was 66.35 cm (26.12 in) at Hoegees station in the San Gabriel Mountains on January 22, 1943.

The other heavy rainstorm period of 1978 occurred from February 27 to March 4, 1978. Mt. Wilson recorded more than 61 cm (24 in) during this period (Fig. 1). The rains of March 4 were particularly intense: La Crescenta, at the foot of the San Gabriel Mountains, received 17.25 (6.79 in) of rain on that day.

In mid-February 1980, a series of six storms occurred over a nine day period. Mt. Wilson received more than 76 cm (30 in) of rain during these storms (Fig. 2) and Topanga Canyon, a residential community in the Santa Monica Mountains, received 43 cm (17 in) (Fig. 3). The Topanga Canyon station recorded 21 cm (8.3 in) in 24 hours on February 17, most of which fell in a 10 hour period. At Bel Air, 8 km away, 8.9 cm (3.5 in) of rain fell in the same 24 hour period, exemplifying the wide variation in precipitation as these storms moved across southern California in relatively narrow belts.

STORM DAMAGE

The City of Los Angeles reported damage at 3,102 addresses during the 1978 winter storms. Los Angeles County, in a less-comprehensive survey of unincorporated areas, reported damage

at 1,796 individual street addresses (Weber and others, 1979). There were 38 storm-related deaths, and $220 million in damages was attributed to the 1978 storms (Brooks, 1982).

Much of the flood damage in mountain and foothill areas occurred in burned watersheds, which produced far more debris than unburned areas (Shuirman and others, 1985). In burned areas, several debris basins—some recently constructed—overflowed, whereas in unburned areas basins proved quite adequate (Brooks, 1982). Extensive areas of the San Gabriel Mountains had been burned in preceding dry periods, and the residential communities below south-facing watersheds were especially vulnerable when the intense storms arrived. In 1978 and 1980, 40% of the estimated 1,720,000 m³ of debris deposited in the debris basins operated by the Los Angeles County Flood Control District was attributed to burned watersheds (Davis, 1982). Zachau, Rubio, and Shields canyons, all within burned watersheds in the southern San Gabriel Mountains, overtopped their debris basins in 1978.

The effect of debris flooding in Shields Canyon is noteworthy. The watershed in this canyon above La Crescenta is only about 0.7 km²; slopes average 1:1. In the 1960s new homes were constructed in the canyon above an older debris basin; a smaller debris basin was built above the new development along with a concrete channel to convey flow through the development to the old basin (Davis, 1982). During the intense storm of February 9–10, 1978, the smaller basin filled to capacity and debris overtopped the structure. The channel, which was too narrow to accommodate debris up to boulder size, became clogged (Fig. 4),

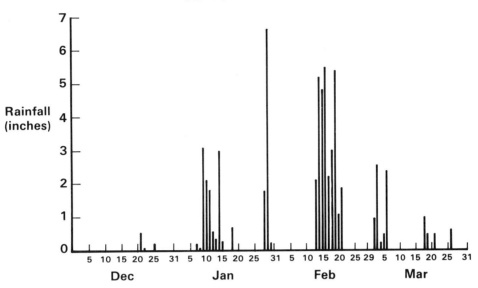

Figure 2. Daily rainfall, December–March, 1979–1980, Mt. Wilson station, NOAA climatological data.

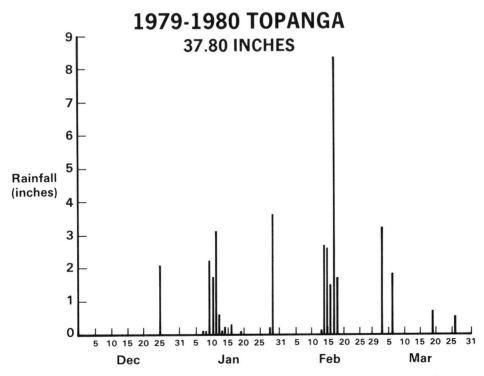

Figure 3. Daily rainfall, December–March, 1979–1980, Topanga station, NOAA climatological data.

Figure 4. Clogged storm drain below debris basin, Shields Canyon, La Crescenta, California. Storm drain is about 3 feet wide.

and flow was diverted out of the channel and onto the street. The high volume of flow and the steep gradient of the street enabled the debris flood to move automobiles parked along the street. Because the street made a right-angle turn just above the old basin, the debris flood left the street and dammed up in the front yard of a single-family residence (Fig. 5).

An event at Hidden Springs on the Middle Fork of Mill Creek in the San Gabriel Mountains was the costliest result of the February 1978 storm in terms of lives lost (Shuirman and others, 1985). A fire in July 1977 burned the entire 10 km^2 watershed of the Middle Fork of Mill Creek. The small resort community and 13 persons were swept away by an estimated 4.5-m-deep flow of water and debris produced by the rains of February 8–10, 1978.

Grass-covered slopes were particularly susceptible to surficial failure during the 1978 storms. Extensive areas of the urbanized foothills are underlain by Miocene marine shales that weather to clay-rich soils that support primarily shallow-rooted grasses (Fig. 6). Debris flows originating in these slopes did extensive damage to residences lacking adequate protective devices or

sufficient setbacks. Even where structures were undamaged, yards were commonly inundated with debris, requiring costly removal.

Debris flows on wooded or chaparral-covered slopes originated chiefly in colluvium-filled ravines. Relatively small failures, starting as slides high on slopes near the heads of natural drainage courses, often became enormous debris flows by the time they reached the base of the slopes. One such failure in a tributary of Benedict Canyon above Beverly Hills incorporated large volumes of ravine-filling material as it moved more than 200 m downslope. The watershed has a relief of about 120 m and an area of about 10 acres, and slopes at the heads of the ravines are 35°–45°, decreasing to 20° at the confluence of the two main branches.

Most of the debris came from the northernmost branch of the tributary (Fig. 7), where failure was observed to have originated on or about February 23, 1978 (E. D. Michael, 1980, personal commun.); the debris had moved about 15 m on a failure surface apparently controlled within bedrock just below the overburden mantle. The 12-m-wide, 3-m-high scarp was about 25 m below the top of the slope, within an area modified

Figure 5. Effects of debris flooding, Shields Canyon, California, February 1978.

Figure 6. Surficial failures on grass-covered slopes, foothills of the San Gabriel Mountains at Big Tujunga Wash, 1978. (Photo courtesy of H. F. Weber, Jr.)

by scarifying the slope of vegetation (Fig. 8). Water seeping from the scarp and the quick condition of part of the debris indicated a near-saturated condition. Saturation and initiation of movement of the slide can probably be attributed to the earlier storm period from February 4–10.

The next series of storms began on February 28, 1978. For the period February 28 to March 4, the nearby upper Stone Canyon station recorded 48.9 cm (19.24 in), of which 20.98 cm (8.26 in) fell on March 4 (Kauper, 1982). Debris flows, which had moved downslope during prior rains, became reactivated by

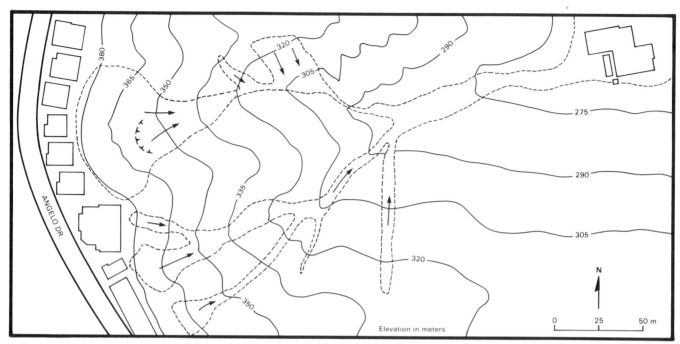

Figure 7. Debris flows originating above Liebe Drive, Santa Monica Mountains (E. D. Michael, 1980, personal commun.). Scarp of initial failure shown in northern tributary.

Figure 8. Scars from debris flows above Liebe Drive, Santa Monica Mountains. Note upper slopes scarified of most large plants. (Photo courtesy of City of Los Angeles, Department of Building and Safety.)

Figure 9. Main channel scoured by debris flow above Liebe Drive, Santa Monica Mountains. (Photo courtesy of City of Los Angeles, Department of Building and Safety.)

the intense downpour of March 4, and up to 4 m of additional ravine fill was scoured from the channels (Fig. 9). An inadequately protected residence, constructed in the axis of the tributary canyon, was inundated with debris (Fig. 10).

Brush removal required to reduce the fire hazard on natural slopes below residences apparently was a significant contributing factor to the initial failure. A bulldozer moving parallel to the slope scarified the brush on the upper 30 m or so of the slope, but also created a ribbon of uncompacted fill surcharging the natural soil and ravine fill along the margin of the scarified zone. The fill was unstable on a slope of 35° to 45°; moreover, the colluvial mantle on the slope above was deprived of stabilizing chaparral. Replanting consisted of shallow-rooted grasses and flowering plants, and surface drainage was uncontrolled.

The 1980 rains caused even more damage than those of 1978, primarily because concentrated, heavy rainfall occurred over a larger area. Deaths attributed to the storms of February 1980 totaled 30, and damages in southern California were estimated at $400 million: 111 homes were destroyed and 1,350 were reported damaged (Weber, 1980). The foothill town of Monterey Park on the eastern edge of the Los Angeles basin underwent extensive damage from debris flows. In older residential areas, many slopes, both natural and artificial, planted with common ice plant failed; new artificial slopes with shallow-rooted ground covers were also susceptible to failure.

The rains and runoff were particularly severe in Topanga

Canyon, washing out the principal roads and isolating the canyon community for several days. Low bridges and imprudent construction practices by local homeowners impeded high discharge and caused flood damage when natural channels overflowed. In Riverside County the San Jacinto River overflowed, and parts of the town of San Jacinto near the river were flooded. Lake Elsinore, receiving waters from the San Jacinto River, rose to unprecedented heights, inundating shoreline homesites.

Greater than normal precipitation also occurred in southern California during the winter of 1982–1983 (more than 76.2 cm [30 in] at Los Angeles Civic Center). However, rainfall was distributed over the season, and short, intense storms comparable to 1978 and 1980 did not occur. A histogram of daily rainfall for Topanga Canyon is shown in Figure 11. Debris flows and debris flooding were uncommon, but 1983 was characterized by deep-seated landslides presumably caused by abnormally high ground-water levels.

GRADING CODES

The first grading code for the City of Los Angeles was established in 1952; however, geologic and soil engineering investigations for residential construction were not required and were rarely sought. Los Angeles County established its first grading code in 1957, Orange County in 1962. Deficiencies in these early codes have periodically been corrected; major revisions in the

Figure 10. Residence at cul-de-sac, Liebe Drive, Santa Monica Mountains, March 1978.

1982-1983 TOPANGA
37.20 INCHES

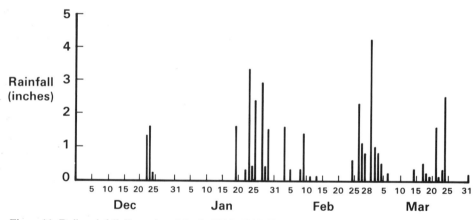

Figure 11. Daily rainfall, December–March, 1982–1983, Topanga station, NOAA climatological data.

City of Los Angeles code were made in 1963, establishing stricter standards and defining better the roles of the geologist and soil engineer. In 1974, California state law required that all permit-issuing agencies within the state adopt Chapter 70 of the Uniform Building Code (UBC) as a minimum; some agencies, notably the City of Los Angeles, maintain even stricter standards. The California Division of Mines and Geology (CDMG) also issued a series of guidelines outlining the elements that should be covered in geologic reports related to development (Slosson, 1984).

Of significance to the following discussion is the treatment of surficial failures in the codes. In 1979, following the severe damage wrought by the 1978 storms, the City of Los Angeles began requiring analyses of surficial failures. For slopes exceeding 2:1, a minimum factor of safety of 1.5 against surficial failure was specified, to be derived by calculations for an infinite slope with seepage parallel to the slope. The use of other methods is subject to approval by the Department of Building and Safety. The minimum assumed depth of soil saturation is 0.9 m (3 ft) or the depth to firm bedrock. Soil strength parameters are to be derived from the testing of representative samples under conditions approximating saturation. The required stability is to be achieved by appropriate mitigating measures.

Slope vegetation requirements for artificial slopes are in Chapter 70 of the UBC; the City of Los Angeles has the same requirements. Slope vegetation should consist of trees with a minimum spacing of 6 m (20 ft), or shrubs spaced 3 m (10 ft) or a combination of the two. Vegetation on natural slopes is not covered in the code. In practice, natural vegetation is commonly removed for fire protection or replaced by shallow-rooted ornamental species.

Mitigation of water and debris flooding is called for in general terms in Chapter 70 of the UBC. Specific provisions are not mentioned, and mitigating measures are expected to fall within "good engineering practice." In recent years, developers of residential tracts have been made responsible for flood-damage control, but the Los Angeles County Flood Control District and the Army Corps of Engineers have assumed responsibilty for protecting most urbanized areas by constructing dams and debris basins.

$$\text{F.S.} = \frac{c' + (\gamma_t - \gamma_w)\, h \cos^2 \alpha \tan \phi'}{\gamma_t\, h \cos \alpha \sin \alpha}$$

γ_t = total, saturated density of soil
γ_w = density of water
h = vertical depth of slide
α = slope angle
c' = effective cohesion
ϕ' = effective friction angle

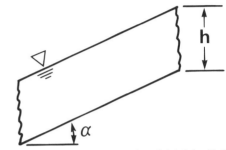

Figure 12. Stability analysis for saturated surficial slab of infinite length. F.S. = factor of safety.

DISCUSSION

The conclusions that can be reached from observing surficial failures during the rainstorms of 1978 and 1980 reinforce those of Campbell's (1975) study of slope failures caused by the 1969 rainstorms in the Santa Monica Mountains. Prerequisites to initiation of debris flows are slopes of 2:1 or greater and a sufficient thickness of soil, colluvium, or poorly consolidated artificial fill. Many fill slopes constructed before updated grading codes were in effect were poorly compacted or were placed on improperly prepared surfaces. Even well-compacted slopes become less well consolidated in time owing to physical and chemical weathering processes and the activity of organisms. Natural slopes in southern California also undergo rapid changes as new soil forms, moves downslope, and accumulates in ravines.

Precipitation sufficient to bring the soil to field moisture capacity (about 25.5 cm [10 in]), followed by a rainstorm with an intensity of greater than 0.63 cm (0.25 in) per hour, constitutes the critical failure criteria (Campbell, 1975). Slosson and Krohn (1982) observed that surficial failures are most severe when heavy rains (more than 25.5 cm [10 in]) occur for five or more days and especially when the most intense rainfall occurs near the end of the storm period.

An analytical model describing the initiation of shallow sliding has been available for many years but has not been commonly applied. Stability analyses of fill slopes constructed under modern grading codes have generally been performed on hypothetical arcuate failure surfaces within the fill, but not on the surficial slab, as shown in Figure 12. This equation, which is derived from the Mohr-Coulomb equation, was discussed in relation to soil failures in the Santa Monica Mountains during the rainstorms of 1969 by Campbell (1975).

When the intensity of rainfall is greater than the ability of the soil or fill to drain, the slope-forming material becomes saturated and seepage proceeded parallel to the slope. The factor of safety for a saturated infinite slope is a function of the effective cohesion, the angle of internal friction, the slope angle, the depth of sliding, and the unit weight of the material.

To illustrate the application of the model to field conditions, the factor of safety calculated using two sets of shear-strength data from tests on saturated samples of shallow failures is plotted in Figure 13; the data suggest that a slope is unstable when the factor of safety is less than 1.5. The sensitivity of the factor of safety to cohesion was emphasized by Gray and Leiser (1982). Figure 14 plots the factor of safety as a function of cohesion for the two sets of data wherein the set of data for artificial slopes includes both failed and unfailed slopes. For this set, an excellent correlation between cohesion and factor of safety exists, largely because the other parameters (slope angle, unit weight, depth of failure and friction angle) are the same or nearly the same for different samples. The set for the natural slopes contains a much wider variation between these parameters—especially slope, which varies from 2:1 to 1:1, and depth of failure, which varies from 0.6 m (2 ft) to 4.6 m (15 ft). Nevertheless, for a factor of safety of 1.5, a minimum cohesion of about 0.10 kg/cm^2 (200 lb/ft^2) is indicated.

Observations of surficial failures in 1978 and 1980 suggest that shallow-rooted vegetation, such as grasses and ice plant, is not effective in preventing surficial failures; such ground covers probably promote soil failures by increasing the infiltration of surface water, thereby leading to "a more rapid and thorough saturation of the soil mantle" (Campbell, 1975).

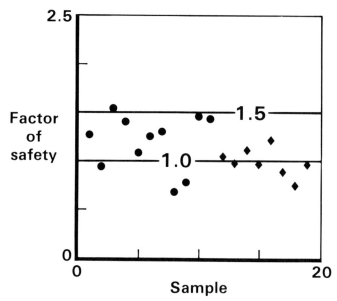

Figure 13. Factor of safety calculated from equation in Figure 12 for failed slopes. Circles: natural slopes (Pascucci, 1985); diamonds: artificial slopes, 2 cuts and 6 fill slopes (unpublished data).

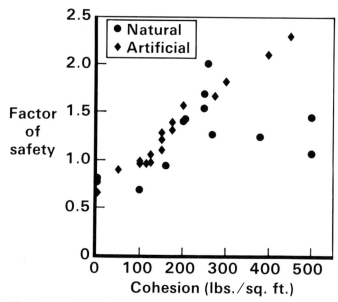

Figure 14. Factor of safety as a function of cohesion. Samples from artificial slopes include failed and unfailed slopes. Highest and lowest values of each data set were not used.

Deep-rooted woody vegetation, however, increases soil strength by root reinforcement and also by the buttressing and soil arching between plants; its removal by fire or clear cutting increases the potential for failure. This cause and effect relation is well documented from studies around the world (Gray and Leiser, 1982). The negative effect of brush fires on surficial slope stability is well known in California (Cleveland, 1973; Davis,

1982). Root reinforcement increases the cohesion and can be added to the numerator of the factor of safety equation (Gray and Leiser, 1982).

Woody plants providing a high concentration of deeply penetrating flexible roots with high tensile strength are most effective for slope stability. Soil shear strength increases with the bulk weight of roots per unit volume, which can also be expressed as the ratio of the area of the roots to the area of the sliding surface. Based on in situ shear test data for sandy residual soil on granitic slopes forested with Douglas Fir, Gray and Leiser (1982) concluded that root-area ratios in the range of 0.05% to 0.10% increased soil shear strength 0.07–0.14 kg/cm^2 (1–2 pounds per square inch or 144–288 lb/ft^2.) An increase in cohesion of 1–2 psi will increase the factor of safety for the slopes in Figure 14 to more than 1.5.

In a study near Cincinnati, Ohio, tree roots increased the factor of safety against shallow sliding ninefold; the sliding surface in this case was the contact between bedrock and colluvium. The average shear strength contributed by tree roots penetrating the contact was determined to be about 0.06 kg/cm^2. In forested areas, colluvium-mantled slopes were stable up to 35°, whereas deforested slopes were subject to sliding at 12° to 14° (Riestenberg and Sovonick-Dunford, 1983).

Studies in the Sam Dimas Experimental Forest near Glendora (Rice and others, 1969) have demonstrated that soil failures are three to five times more frequent for grass-covered slopes than for brush-covered slopes, and the minimum angles for failure were less for grassy cover than for most chaparral. Studies of the root systems of southern California chaparral suggest that the most favorable native species, owing to their deeply penetrating root systems, are Eastwood manzanita (*Arctostaphylos glandulosa* Eastwood), live oaks, Christmasberry (*Photinia arbutifolia* [Ait.] Lindl.) and, to a somewhat lesser extent, chamise (*Adenostoma fasciculatum* H. & A.) and chaparral whitethorn (*Ceanothus leucodermis* Greene) (Hellmers and others, 1955). The root system of the California scrub oak (*Quercus dumosa* Nutt.) (Fig. 15) penetrates as much as 8 m (25 ft) into fractured bedrock, but also spread laterally, thus reinforcing the colluvial layer.

Buttressing is provided by firmly anchored tree trunks or large diameter shrubs. Arching occurs when soil attempts to move through and around a row of trees (Gray and Leiser, 1982). If the rows are staggered, the buttressing and arching affects a large proportion of the slope (Fig. 16).

Fatalities occurred during the 1978 and 1980 rainstorms in homes built close to the base of a steep, soil-mantled slope and, in the majority of cases, were caused by debris flows originated on slopes vegetated with grasses, ice plant, or other shallow-rooted ground covers. In some cases, deep-rooted native growth was removed for fire protection and replaced with shallow-rooted ornamental species. Swales or natural ravines concentrating flows toward home sites produced an additional hazard.

The effect of strengthened grading codes has been encouraging. A survey of 37,000 sites graded before 1963 in the City of Los Angeles showed 2,790 failures, or 7.5%, whereas 36,000 sites

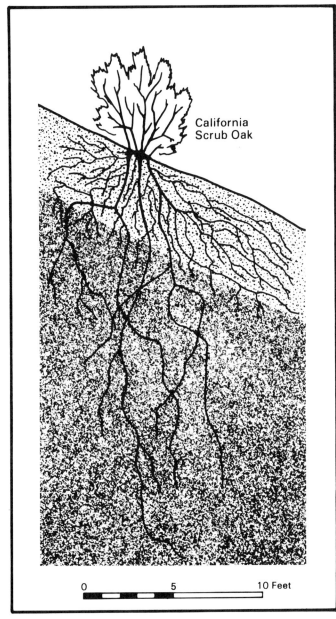

Figure 15. Root system of California scrub oak (*Quercus dumosa* Nutt.), after Hellmers and others (1955).

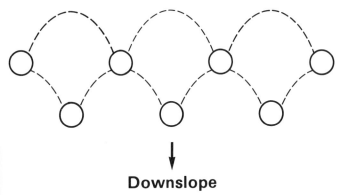

Figure 16. Buttressing and arching effect of trees or large shrubs (adapted from Gray and Leiser, 1982).

graded after 1963 had 210 failures, or 0.07% (Slosson and Krohn, 1982). Until recently, stability analyses were not performed to investigate the potential for surficial failures. The City and County of Los Angeles now require that the potential for surficial slope failures be assessed as part of the geotechnical investigation. Some other permit-issuing agencies, however, do not even require geologic studies. The vegetation requirements in Chapter 70 of the UBC are not generally adhered to; hydromulching of fill slopes with grass seed, which is not in compliance with the code, is common practice. Moreover, it is questionable whether the code, which calls for trees to be spaced at 6 m (20 ft) and shrubs

at 3 m (10 ft), is adequate. Spacing should be such that the slope is covered with a continuous canopy of trees or shrubs with root systems sufficient to reinforce surficial unconsolidated materials and to bind them to firmer substrate.

Burned watersheds yield far greater amounts of water and debris runoff than unburned areas. The vegetal canopy and some of the shallower root systems are destroyed, resulting in greater erosion by raindrop impact and surface flow. Moreover, increased soil creep between rains produces deeper ravine fill for movement during ensuing storms (Simpson, 1969). The intense heat of fires produces a hydrophobic layer just below the surface, an impervious waxy substance formed from organic matter in the soil, which is believed to contribute significantly to increased runoff (Cleveland, 1973).

Observations of the 1978 and 1980 rainstorms showed that debris basins were not designed to accommodate the increased debris that results when brush fires precede such storms within two to three years. In addition, many privately engineered flood-control provisions in residential tracts proved to be underdesigned, and drainage provisions were commonly neglected. Developers of housing tracts are required to install bench drains, collection basins, berms, and other devices to convey water quickly away from slopes, however, when the homes are completed, responsibility for maintaining the devices passes to the homeowners, who seldom make a coordinated effort to maintain devices common to several properties. The devices become clogged and fail to function when the need arises.

Studies of the 1978 and 1980 rainstorms have made geologists and soil engineers more aware of the causes of surficial failures. Slopes with the potential for surficial failure can be more clearly identified; grading codes need to be updated to reflect this knowledge and enforced. Stability analyses for the surficial slab should be performed on both natural and engineered fill slopes that may affect new developments. Structural mitigative measures, such as debris fences and deflection walls (Gray and Leiser, 1982; Chin, 1985), have proven to be effective and can be constructed at relatively low cost. Planting deep-rooted trees or large shrubs is even less costly.

Special slope stability studies of existing developments in areas known to be sensitive to slope failure are appropriate tasks for state and local governments. Site-specific investigations by private consultants when property ownership is transferred alerts sellers and buyers to potential geologic hazards that can usually be minimized or abated at modest cost in comparison to the value of the property. Further education of the public on slope hazards, including the maintenance of mutually owned drainage devices and the planting of proper slope vegetation, is recommended.

ACKNOWLEDGMENTS

I thank D. L. Lamar, Lamar-Merifield Geologists, Inc.; E. D. Michael, Consulting Geologist, Malibu, California; J. W. Cobarrubias, Los Angeles City Geologist, and A. G. Keene, Los Angeles County Geologist, for their comments.

REFERENCES CITED

Brooks, N. H., 1982, Overview and summary, in Jennings, P. C., and Brooks, N. H., eds., Storms, floods, and debris flows in southern California and Arizona 1978 and 1980: Washington, D.C., National Academy Press, p. 1–24.

Campbell, R. H., 1975, Soil slips, debris flows, and rainstorms in the Santa Monica Mountains and vicinity, southern California: U.S. Geological Survey Professional Paper 851, 51 p.

Chin, A. E., 1985, Landslide and debris flow hazard mitigation measures for existing development, in Bowles, D. S., ed., Delineation of landslide, flash flood, and debris flow hazards in Utah: Logan, Utah State University, Utah Water Resources Laboratory, General Series UWRL/G-85/03, p. 511–531.

Cleveland, G. B., 1973, Fire + rain = mudflows, Big Sur, 1972: California Geology, v. 26, p. 127–135.

Davis, J. D., 1982, Rare and unusual postfire flood events experienced in Los Angeles County during 1978 and 1980, in Jennings, P. C., and Brooks, N. H., eds., Storms, floods, and debris flows in southern California and Arizona 1978 and 1980: Washington, D.C., National Academy Press, p. 243–256.

Gray, D. H., and Leiser, A. T., 1982, Biotechnical slope protection and erosion control: New York, Van Nostrand Reinhold Company, 271 p.

Hellmers, H., Horton, J. S., Juhren, G., and O'Keefe, J., 1955, Root systems of some chaparral plants in southern California: Ecology, v. 36, no. 4, p. 667–678.

Kauper, E. K., 1982, Meteorological report on conditions existing over the eastern Santa Monica Mountains, February 28 through March 4, 1978: Covina, California, Metro Monitoring Services, 11 p.

Pascucci, V. N., 1985, 475 landslides in the City of Pacifica, California, in Bowles, D. S., ed., Delineation of landslide, flash flood, and debris flow hazards in Utah: Logan, Utah State University, Utah Water Resources Laboratory, General Series UWRL/G-85/03, p. 99–112.

Pyke, C., 1982, Return periods of 1977–80 precipitation in southern California and Arizona, in Jennings, P. C., and Brooks, N. H., eds., Storms, floods, and debris flows in southern California and Arizona 1978 and 1980: Washington, D.C., National Academy Press, p. 77–86.

Rice, R. M., Corbett, E. S., and Bailey, R. G., 1969, Soil slips related to vegetation, topography and soil in southern California: Water Resources Research, v. 5, no. 3, p. 647–658.

Riestenberg, M. M., and Sovonick-Dunford, S., 1983, The role of woody vegetation in stabilizing slopes in the Cincinnati area, Ohio: Geological Society of America Bulletin, v. 94, p. 506–518.

Shuirman, G., Slosson, J. E., and Yoakum, D., 1985, Relationship of fire/flood to debris flows, in Bowles, D. S., ed., Delineation of landslide, flash flood, and debris flow hazards in Utah: Logan, Utah State University, Utah Water Resources Laboratory, General Series UWRL/G-85/03, p. 178–194.

Simpson, L. D., 1969, Hydrologic report on storms of 1969: Los Angeles, California, County Flood Control District, 286 p.

Slosson, J. E., 1984, Genesis and evolution of guidelines for geologic reports: Bulletin of the Association of Engineering Geologists, v. 31, p. 295–316.

Slosson, J. E., and Krohn, J. P., 1982, Southern California landslides of 1978 and 1980, in southern California and Arizona, in Jennings, P. C., and Brooks, N. H., eds., Storms, floods, and debris flows in southern California and Arizona 1978 and 1980: Washington, D.C., National Academy Press, p. 291–320.

Weber, F. H., 1980, Landsliding and flooding in southern California during the winter of 1979–1980: California Division of Mines and Geology Open-File Report 80-3LA, 69 p.

Weber, F. H., Treiman, J. A., Tan, S. S., and Miller, R. V., 1979, Landslides in the Los Angeles region, California—Effects of February-March 1978 rains: California Division of Mines and Geology Open-File report 79-4LA, 265 p.

MANUSCRIPT ACCEPTED BY THE SOCIETY FEBRUARY 21, 1992

Geological Society of America
Reviews in Engineering Geology, Volume IX
1992

Chapter 3

The concept of 'reasonable care' on unstable hillsides

Robert B. Olshansky*
Rogers/Pacific, Inc., 396 Civic Drive, Pleasant Hill, California 94523
J. David Rogers
Rogers/Pacific, Inc., 396 Civic Drive, Pleasant Hill, California 94523

ABSTRACT

The old common-law rules of strict liability with regard to earth movement have given way to the more modern legal doctrine of "reasonable care" in the California court system, which hears the largest number of earth movement–related cases in the United States. Reasonable care doctrine is more case specific, and emanates from the legal definition of "negligence," or the exercise of responsible conduct for which a professional is always held accountable, regardless of liability-limitation agreements. Three landmark California decisions are briefly profiled, including the most recent, in which the California State Supreme Court ruled that it is common knowledge that all fill embankments will settle, just as rotten trees or dilapidated buildings can be expected to collapse. The chapter concludes with the implications for geopractitioners in today's ever-evolving legal climate.

INTRODUCTION

Over the past two decades, judicial decisions involving earth-surface processes have trended toward rejecting many of the old common law rules of liability. The courts are moving away from specific doctrines of liability and toward more case-specific applications of the idea of "reasonable care" (Olshansky and Rogers, 1987).

The term "reasonable care" is closely related to the legal definition of negligence, generally defined as the failure to exercise the degree of care appropriate to a situation. Whether a person has been "reasonable" depends on the facts of the case. *Black's law dictionary* (1990) defined "reasonable care" as follows: "That degree of care which a person of ordinary prudence would exercise in the same or similar circumstances. . . .Due care under all the circumstances. Failure to exercise such care is ordinary negligence." Hence, both "negligence" and "reasonable care" are relative terms that must be judged for each situation. The judgment of whether an actor has behaved "reasonably" is up to a jury, according to the testimony presented to them.

This chapter illustrates the recent trends in the law with three California cases: *Keys v. Romley* (California Supreme Court, 1966), *Sprecher v. Adamson* (California Supreme Court, 1981), and *Easton v. Strassburger et al.* (California Appellate Court, 1984).

SURFACE WATER: *KEYS V. ROMLEY*

Surface water law

The case of *Keys v. Romley* (California Supreme Court, 1966) changed the law of surface water in California, and is therefore of obvious importance to landslide cases. In this decision, California followed Minnesota, New Hampshire, and New Jersey in adopting the "rule of reasonable use" of surface water. This rule has since been adopted by at least eight additional states (Tank, 1983).

To understand the rule of reasonable use, one must first examine the other two doctrines of surface water law in the United States, the "common enemy doctrine" and the "civil law rule" (Kinyon and McClure, 1940). The common enemy doctrine states that a landowner has an unqualified right to fend off surface water from his property, irrespective of the downhill effect; each landowner is responsible only to himself in diverting the water off his property. The civil law rule is a modification of

---

*Present-address: Department of Urban and Regional Planning, University of Illinois, Urbana, Illinois 61801.

Olshansky, R. B., and Rogers, J. D., 1992, The concept of 'reasonable care' on unstable hillsides, *in* Slosson, J. E., Keene, A. G., and Johnson, J. A., eds., Landslides/Landslide Mitigation: Boulder, Colorado, Geological Society of America Reviews in Engineering Geology, v. IX.

the common enemy doctrine. This rule states that the lower land-owner must accept drainage from above, as under the common enemy doctrine, but the upper owner may not modify the natural flow so as to increase the downhill burden. This rule, a clear statement that the upper owner may not divert natural flow, to the detriment of those below, was the law in California prior to *Keys v. Romley.*

The case

The *Keys v. Romley* case concerned two properties in Walnut Creek, Contra Costa County. In 1956, Keys built an appliance store. Construction involved some excavation and piling of the spoils at the rear of the property. In 1957, Romley constructed a roller-skating rink above and behind the appliance store (Fig. 1). This construction involved grading, leveling, paving, and the placement of four roof downspouts that directed runoff onto Keys's property. In 1957, Keys built a parking area and added to the soil pile. In the autumn of 1958, Keys removed this pile. Between January 1959 and January 1962, Keys's appliance store was flooded repeatedly, despite attempts to divert surface water. Finally, in 1962, by mutual agreement after litigation had begun, Romley constructed a concrete curb on the property line, to prevent flow onto Keys's property. The lower court enjoined Romley from interfering with the natural flow of water to Keys's detriment, based on the civil law rule. The court also awarded $4,384.78 in damages to Keys. The California Supreme Court reversed this decision, however, using this case as the opportunity to adopt the rule of reasonable use.

The rule of reasonable use applies to both uphill and downhill owners, requiring uphill owners to take reasonable care when diverting surface water and requiring downhill owners to take reasonable precautions to avoid injury and damage from surface water. The *Keys v. Romley* court declared that surface-water cases should not be decided by an unvarying rule, but rather by the facts of the particular case, as determined by a jury. The *Keys v. Romley* case was therefore sent back to the trial court for a decision.

It is often the case in major judicial decisions that the factual situation does not appear to warrant a landmark decision. Historically, a court knows what changes it would like to make in the law, and it takes the first suitable case that comes its way. Such appears to be the situation in *Keys v. Romley.* The facts, as reported in the Supreme Court decision, strongly suggest to most readers that the balance of reasonableness lies in favor of Keys (who would also have won the case under the civil law rule). This case does not appear to be particularly unique nor worthy as a foundation for a new legal theory, but it provided the court of that era (1966) with a case upon which to build the doctrine of reasonableness. Indeed, according to Keys's attorney (J. Ganong, 1986, personal commun.), when it was returned to the trial court, the case was decided in Keys's favor after a brief hearing.

The rule of reasonable use is, to attorneys, subtly different from the older negligence concept of reasonable care. To the rest

Figure 1. Present-day view of the site of the *Keys v. Romley* case. Keys's electronics store fronted on the main boulevard in the foreground, and Romley's ice-skating rink was situated on the hill above and behind him.

of us, however, the concepts appear quite similar. This reasonableness rule forever erased absolute tests or definite rules for liability exposure from surface-water damages. Rather, each case is to be decided on its own merits, based on the behavior of the players involved, the apparent gravity of the harm, the respective duties owed to one another, and the knowledge each had or should have had.

NATURAL SLOPES: *SPRECHER V. ADAMSON*

Natural conditions: The law

It is an old common-law rule that an owner of natural unimproved land is immune from liability for the effects of the condition of his land on off-site persons or property. If a damaging landslide is related to artificial conditions, then the uphill owner can be tried for negligence on the basis of the reasonableness of his behavior (or inaction) and the connection of his behavior to the onset of land slippage. But, if the landslide occurs on natural, unaltered land, then there was no basis for legal action. This reasoning is analogous to the civil law rule of surface waters described above.

There has generally been an exception to this rule in regard to decaying trees that fall and cause injury on neighboring properties (New York Supreme Court, 1896; Noel, 1943). This is because courts of past eras believed that it is relatively easy to recognize decaying trees and remove what is intrinsically a significant hazard to neighbors, particularly in urban areas. An increasing number of states have declared such an exception to the rule in these cases.

The case

Sprecher v. Adamson (California Supreme Court, 1981) was a case involving a landslide in the Malibu beach area of Los Angeles County. The Adamson Companies owned a 90 acre parcel of unimproved land uphill from Old Malibu Road. The parties in the case did not dispute the fact that Adamson's land was natural and was on part of a periodically active ancient landslide complex that had been recognized for many decades. Sprecher lived in a beachfront house across Malibu Road from the Adamson property, at the toe of the landslide (Fig. 2).

In March 1978, following heavy rain, portions of the ancient slide complex above Sprecher reactivated, pushing Sprecher's house and causing it to rotate slightly and press against his neighbor's house. The neighbor, Sexton, filed suit against Sprecher, and Sprecher filed suit against Sexton, the Adamson Companies, and Los Angeles County (they were responsible for the roads, and also for approving caisson piers Sexton had installed to protect her property). The cases between Sprecher and Sexton were settled by their insurance carriers, and the trial court found in favor of the county. The California Supreme Court case was Sprecher's appeal of the decision declaring the Adamson Companies to be immune and not subject to trial because of the traditional common law immunity from damage claims for owners of unimproved properties.

The California Supreme Court decision in *Sprecher v. Adamson* discarded the common law immunity and declared that each case must be tried on its own merits, according to the principles of negligence (Okhansky, 1990). Hence, the Supreme Court required the trial court to decide whether the Adamson

Figure 2. Aerial oblique view looking west, down Old Malibu Road, at the site of the landslide resulting in the *Sprecher v. Adamson* case. The undeveloped slope at right was an ancient bedrock landslide complex owned by the Adamson Company. It reactivated in the early spring of 1978, pushing against the beach-front homes owned by Sexton and Sprecher. Note the bend in the road alignment at the slide's western limits.

Companies exercised reasonable care, considering all the circumstances (likelihood of injury to plaintiff, probable seriousness of such injury, the cost of reducing or avoiding the risk, the location of the land, and the landowner's degree of control over the condition). This case was sent back to the trial court with that instruction.

As with *Keys v. Romley,* the facts of the case would seem to make it an unlikely candidate for such a significant decision. Many geologists were shocked by the facts of this case, because the ancient slide complex was too large for Adamson to reasonably stabilize, and they mistakenly believe that the decision declared Adamson's negligence. Although it was a major legal decision, its only effect on this particular case was to specify the rules for a second trial. The end result of *Sprecher v. Sexton* as with *Keys v. Romley* supports what most of us interpret as the facts of the case. The case never even went to trial on the second round: it was settled for $10,000, which was a token amount compared to what the additional trial costs would have been. The willingness to settle for such a small amount suggests that both parties expected Adamson to prevail had it been taken to trial.

This decision has been widely criticized, primarily because of the faulty analogy the Supreme Court drew between decaying trees and landslides (for example, Slosson, 1983; Burcham, 1983). Such reasoning has not been followed by other states. Still, it is a significant part of the recent trend toward discarding old common law rules in favor of the negligence idea of "reasonable care," an idea increasingly promoted by trial attorneys who are working for imperiled plaintiffs (Olshansky, 1990).

REALTORS: *EASTON V. STRASSBURGER*

Easton v. Strassburger (California Appelate Court, 1984) was a California Appellate Court decision that expanded the duties of realtors and the grounds for realtor negligence in selling faulty homes. The California State Supreme Court declined to hear the case, thereby giving the decision the force of law in the state.

The Strassburgers owned a home and adjacent property in Diablo, Contra Costa County (Fig. 3). It appears that the home was originally constructed on a combination cut-fill pad without benefit of sufficient keying and benching of the fill. The fill underwent a minor slide in 1973 adjacent to the house, followed by a major slide of the same area in 1975. When the Strassburgers sold the property in 1976 to Easton, they did not disclose the slides or their subsequent repairs. Soon after purchasing the home, there were additional slides and settlement in the fill in 1976, 1977, and 1978. Easton filed suit against the Strassburgers, the contractors, the realtors, and three other parties. The trial court found all of the defendants negligent and apportioned 65% to the Strassburgers and 5% to the realtors. The realtors' appeal of that decision is the basis of this case.

The Appellate Court upheld the decision against the realtors, who were deceived by the Strassburgers, just as Easton was. The court held, however, that realtors, as licensed professionals,

Figure 3. A: Overview of the Easton home, situated in the community of Diablo, Contra Costa County, California. B: Ground view at brow of the fill slope behind the Easton home. It was this slope that had supposedly settled. The California Supreme Court found the realtor guilty on the premise that they should have made themselves aware of the settling problem by simply viewing the slope in combination with the knowledge that the home was built upon fill. The court did not accept any expert testimony from geotechnical professionals regarding the veracity of such a premise.

have a duty to not only disclose what they know, but also what they, as professionals, should know, making "reasonable use" of their knowledge, skills, and experience. In the eyes of the court, the realtors saw and ignored so-called "red flags" (such as the mere presence of fill, uneven floors, and erosion netting placed on slopes) that should have alerted them, as experienced realtors, to potential problems (Fig. 3). The court held that realtors have an affirmative duty to further investigate such obvious signs of distress.

The *Easton v. Strassburger* case has spawned a whole new procedure for disclosure in California home sales. The California Association of Realtors developed disclosure forms to verify that the sellers have fully notified buyers of all defects, hopefully reducing the exposure of realtors to litigation. These disclosure forms have since been legislated into state law. An ironic footnote to this case is that the current owners of this property, which is still undergoing slope movement problems, were unaware of its history when they purchased it.

CONCLUSIONS

In summary, the concept of "reasonable care" has become more important in earth movement and surface-water cases as the grounds for negligence have increased. The determination of what is reasonable is for a jury to decide, based largely on often-contradictory expert testimony.

The vagueness of the law in this area creates a difficult situation for geologists and engineers. There is little guidance from the courts as to what constitutes reasonable care. However, it is not a question of law, to be determined by a judge, but a question of fact, decided by a jury. The legal trends actually make geologic sense. They promote case-by-case review and say that there are no absolute rules; it is also true of natural hillsides and streams. But, despite the Earth's lack of homogeneity, we do need common standards and guidelines for each actor. The current legal climate creates an opportunity for geologists to educate attorneys, property owners, realtors, and ourselves. What warning signs indicate problems? What is "reasonable care" for hillside property owners? What are reasonable maintenance and landscaping practices? What constitutes a reasonable site investigation?

Geologists should consider these questions and begin publishing guidelines. Such professionally accepted standards would carry a great deal of weight in expert testimony, and would help to define for juries what the state of knowledge and standards of profession are (Olshansky, 1989). Rather than complain about legal trends, this is a chance for the profession to take action and clarify some questions for ourselves, the courts, and the public.

REFERENCES CITED

Black, H. C., 1990, Black's law dictionary (6th edition): St. Paul, Minnesota, West Publishing Co., 1657 p.

Burcham, 1983, Sprecher v. Adamson Companies: Nonfeasance immunity slides by the California Supreme Court: Loyola Los Angeles Law Review, v. 16, p. 625.

California Appellate Courts, 1984, Easton versus Strassburger et al.: California Reports (third edition), v. 152: San Francisco, California, West Publishing Co., p. 90.

California Supreme Court, 1966, Keys versus Romley decision: California Reports (second edition), v. 64: San Francisco, California, West Publishing Co., p. 396.

California Supreme Court, 1981, Sprecher versus Adamson Companies et al.: California Reports (third edition), v. 30: San Francisco, California, West Publishing Co., p. 358.

Kinyon, S. V., and McClure, R. C., 1940, Interferences with surface waters: Minnesota Law Review, v. 24, p. 891–939.

New York Supreme Court, 1896, Gibson versus Denton: New York State Reporter, v. 38, p. 554.

Noel, D. W., 1943, Nuisances from land in its natural condition: Harvard Law Review, v. 56, p. 772.

Olshansky, R. B., 1989, Landslide Hazard Reduction: A need for greater government involvement, Zoning and Planning Law Report, v. 12, no. 3, March.

—— , 1990, Landslide hazard in the United States: Case studies in planning and policy development: New York, Garland Publishing, Inc., 176 p.

Olshansky, R. B., and Rogers, J. D., 1987, Unstable ground: Landslide policy in the United States: Ecology Law Quarterly, v. 13, no. 4, p. 939–1006.

Slosson, J., 1983, Sprecher v. Adamson Companies: A critique of the Supreme Court decision: Real Property Law Reporter, v. 6, p. 117–120.

Tank, R. W., 1983, Legal aspects of geology: New York, Plenum Press, 186 p.

MANUSCRIPT ACCEPTED BY THE SOCIETY FEBRUARY 21, 1992

Geological Society of America
Reviews in Engineering Geology, Volume IX
1992

Chapter 4

Differentiation between normal residence performance and landslide-related distress in the evaluation and treatment of slope instability in southern California

Hugh S. Robertson
Robertson Geotechnical, Inc., 2500 Townsgate Road, Suite E, Westlake Village, California 91361
Robert A. Hollingsworth
Grover-Hollingsworth and Associates, 31129 Via Colinas, Suite 707, Westlake Village, California 91362

ABSTRACT

The evaluation and repair of hillside properties damaged by slope instability presents a challenging problem for the geotechnical professional. An increasing number of residential distress evaluations are being requested by homeowner insurance companies to resolve earth-movement claims. Early recognition of instability is essential to the successful mitigation of the hazard. Thorough observation of structural distress, experience, and an understanding of construction are needed to differentiate typical distress from subtle distress associated with the initiation of slope instability. Other soil-related processes cause distress similar in appearance to major slope movement, and complicate recognition of an impending hazard.

Property-line limitations and reluctant neighbors hamper site and neighborhood reconnaissance. High costs and physical constraints limit the subsurface exploration, which is critical to determining the mechanics of movement. Conventional exploration techniques are aided by modern instrumentation and detailed site monitoring to define probable causes. Selection of reasonable repair methods and stabilization devices depends on the limits of the failing mass and whether instability is associated with failure along a predetermined defect or through an inherently weak mass. Continued monitoring from recognition through stabilization helps verify the causes of instability, the design scheme, and the success of the treatment. Repairs are effective if the factor of safety is sufficiently increased by common and economical construction techniques in a timely manner.

INTRODUCTION

Insurance companies have become more involved during recent years in evaluating landslide and settlement distress of residential properties. The insurance policies of most homeowners specifically exclude earth movement as a covered loss. However, various court rulings from the early 1960s to present have resulted in coverage for earth movement under an "all risk" homeowners policy. Geotechnical evaluations are commissioned by the insurance companies to assist in the resolution of claims for residential damage reportedly caused by earth movement. Coverage determination requires information on the character of distress, causes of distress, and methods to stabilize the property. This has greatly increased the number and frequency of property evaluations by geotechnical consultants.

Property evaluations present an interesting and challenging problem for the geotechnical professional. Distress is often very subtle. Experience is needed to differentiate subtle distress caused by the initiation of slope movement from typical distress associated with other soil-related processes such as fill settlement

Robertson, H. S., and Hollingsworth, R. A., 1992, Differentiation between normal residence performance and landslide-related distress in the evaluation and treatment of slope instability in southern California, *in* Slosson, J. E., Keene, A. G., and Johnson, J. A., eds., Landslides/Landslide Mitigation: Boulder, Colorado, Geological Society of America Reviews in Engineering Geology, v. IX.

and heaving of expansive soil. The investigation requires a thorough evaluation of structural distress tempered with an understanding of construction techniques. Adequate exploration can be difficult, but is essential for successful stabilization. A successful repair program is dependent upon early recognition of the nature of the problem and accurate determination of the mechanics of the movement and limits of the failing mass.

NORMAL VS. UNUSUAL CONSTRUCTION PERFORMANCE

Cracking and irregularities occur with all forms of construction due to typical performance of building materials, soil movement, and deterioration. Successful identification of slope instability requires the geotechnical professional to differentiate normal construction performance from cracking and irregularities caused by slope movement. Construction materials react differently to changes in temperature, weather, and time. They also react differently to various forms of soil movement. The cracking and irregularities caused by these various processes, however, can be surprisingly similar.

Building process

The framing of a single-family residence is not a perfect process. The finished product is a function of both the performance of the wood and the degree of care taken by the builder. Wood framing can be distorted by wind during the construction process. If the distortion is not corrected prior to placing wall board and stucco, the irregularities are built into the home. Experience indicates that a tract home, built simultaneously with a number of homes by large crews, has a higher risk of irregularity than a custom home. In addition, the time spent on construction can control the amount of wall cracking that develops. Speedy construction is more prone to cracking because the ground and structure are not allowed sufficient time to adjust to loading and curing of wood and cement products. Cosmetic treatments such as paint and wallpaper are more prone to crack in a quickly constructed home.

Cracking and irregularities of dry wall and plaster construction cannot be eliminated. Construction techniques can increase the propensity for cracking. An improperly loaded roof during construction can cause stresses within the structure that can result in cracking after the roof is installed and stresses are redistributed. Common irregularities due to improper roof loading include buckling of dry-wall tape seams and corners.

Wood

Wood used in framing and decorative treatments shrinks during aging and drying. The amount of shrinkage depends on a number of factors, including, but not limited to, the type of the wood, the milling process, and the curing time prior to milling and distribution. Wood shrinkage can be significant. Shrinkage

can result in apparent settlement of more than 1 in (2.54 cm) on three-story wood-frame construction. Obvious gaps can develop between exposed wood beams and plaster and stucco walls. Wood beams can twist when drying after construction, causing cracking of adjacent walls. Shrinkage of wood moldings and door frames can cause gaps between the wood and the wall. This type of cracking and irregularity is cosmetic and, over a period of time, becomes less noticeable due to painting. Gaps and irregularities between wood and stucco and plaster walls are common occurrences and often thought by owners to be indicative of foundation and land movement.

Wood floors develop irregularities due to shrinkage and deflection. Floor joists can deflect before and after loading, creating depressions in the floor. Shrinkage of the joists can cause floor irregularities. Floor irregularities can also occur when wood and steel elements are used together. The floor irregularities caused by these processes can be noticeable and disturbing to the homeowner.

Concrete

Concrete products shrink during curing, typically causing cracking. Nearly all slabs in single-family homes exhibit some type of cracking (Fig. 1). The severity of the cracking can be a function of the ratio of water and cement, the aggregate size, the rate of drying, and the placement technique. The processes leading to concrete-slab cracking cannot be eliminated, but can be reduced by proper reinforcement and meticulous concrete placement. Poor construction techniques can result in obvious and significant cracking, which can be misinterpreted as an indication of soil movement.

Shrinkage can be minimized through concrete design. A high-strength, low-moisture concrete with a 1 in (2.54 cm) top size aggregate has been used to minimize shrinkage cracking. Such a concrete mix is more difficult and costly to place. Water is not added to facilitate placement, but a superplasticizer can be used. The mixture is difficult to pump and often requires placement by hand. Utilizing the high-strength, low-moisture concrete mixes does not guarantee that shrinkage cracks will not develop. Steel reinforcement is recommended to significantly minimize unusual cracking or differential movement, but it has to be properly placed.

Shrinkage cracking generally takes four forms: diagonal cracking across corners, linear cracking across the central one-third of large expanses of concrete, linear cracking adjacent to exterior walls, and small polygonal cracking (Fig. 1). Diagonal cracking is common due to greater resistance to shrinkage in the corner of a room. Linear cracking is common in concrete sections with widths greater than about 4.6 to 6.1 m (15 to 20 ft). The location of the shrinkage crack can be controlled by drain lines, location of steel reinforcing bars, or utility outlets that penetrate the slab. Exterior flat work is generally provided with expansion joints, which control the location of the shrinkage cracking. Placing expansion joints on interior slabs is not a com-

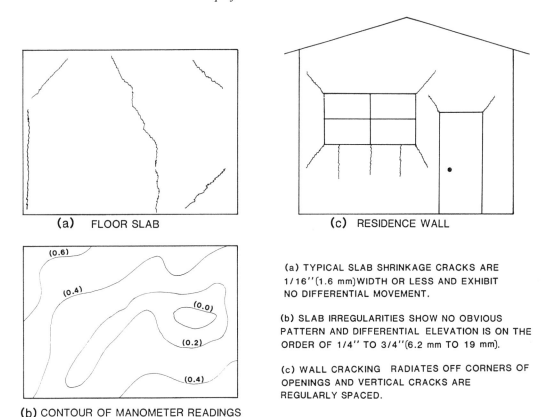

(a) FLOOR SLAB

(b) CONTOUR OF MANOMETER READINGS

(c) RESIDENCE WALL

(a) TYPICAL SLAB SHRINKAGE CRACKS ARE 1/16"(1.6 mm)WIDTH OR LESS AND EXHIBIT NO DIFFERENTIAL MOVEMENT.

(b) SLAB IRREGULARITIES SHOW NO OBVIOUS PATTERN AND DIFFERENTIAL ELEVATION IS ON THE ORDER OF 1/4" TO 3/4"(6.2 mm TO 19 mm).

(c) WALL CRACKING RADIATES OFF CORNERS OF OPENINGS AND VERTICAL CRACKS ARE REGULARLY SPACED.

Figure 1. Normal cosmetic cracking and irregularities due to construction techniques and typical performance of construction materials.

mon construction technique. Linear cracking commonly occurs near walls because the edge of the slab is restrained by the wall weight. Near the latter stages of curing, small, hairline polygonal cracks can occur throughout the slab section as the subgrade soil and concrete dries. Curing of concrete can take a number of years. Major shrinkage cracking tends to develop during the first six months after pouring. Development of additional shrinkage cracks will continue to occur over 2 to 3 years.

Steel reinforcement is intended to reduce cracking. Wire mesh is the minimum reinforcement requirement, but can be of limited effectiveness unless placed in the central or upper one-third of the slab section. Reinforcement must be placed on blocks to ensure its proper location in the slab, but this is difficult to accomplish and generally not done. Instead, the wire is pulled up into the concrete after pouring. Experience indicates that wire mesh generally remains near the bottom or beneath the slab and is therefore of limited effectiveness. Steel reinforcing bars provide a more positive method of reinforcement, but are more costly and time consuming to place. Blocking a grid of reinforcing bars is easier and does not hamper pouring of the slab.

Placement of concrete for slab floors results in irregularities that cannot be eliminated. Doming, depressions, and slopes are common for slabs. Differential elevation changes across a new slab floor commonly range from 0.25 to 0.75 in (6.2 to 19.0 mm). Irregularities greater than 0.75 in (19.0 mm) can generally be noticed by walking on the floor and may be corrected during the construction process.

Ceramic tile

Ceramic tile is a brittle construction material and prone to cracking. The propensity of concrete slabs to develop shrinkage cracking presents a problem when a ceramic tile is placed on the slab without an adequate mortar bed. It is common to place ceramic tile on slab floor by gluing the tile onto the slab. This procedure increases the risk of hairline cracking of the adhered tile that mirrors the shrinkage cracking.

Stucco and plaster

Plaster and stucco are cement products and are subject to normal cracking. The most typical stucco crack pattern is diagonal cracking radiating off the corners of window and door openings (Fig. 1). The cracking develops at the corners due to shrinkage during curing. Stucco will often develop a series of regularly spaced, vertical cracks that occur along studs. The severity of cracking is controlled by the ratio of cement and water. Improper curing of different layers of the stucco can also result in periodic cracking of the finished coat.

It is not unusual to get moderate to severe cracking above

the service door for the garage because of the lack of paneling on the inside of the garage. The lack of a shear panel increases the propensity for movement. Service doors are commonly placed near the contact of the garage footing and the residence footing, which are normally not tied together. Differential settlement between the two foundations can result in adjustments of the structure and cracking over the door, which is the weak point on the wall.

Existing effects

Once cracking has occurred, a defect has been created. Future movement or adjustments of the residence will often magnify the cracking and irregularities. Normal settlement of a structure, movement due to changes in the live load or the wind load, or adjustments of the structure due to subtle soil movements tend to widen and lengthen the cosmetic cracking common to all wood frame and stucco construction. The character, pattern, and magnitude of the cracking must therefore be carefully considered in the geotechnical evaluation.

RECOGNIZING LANDSLIDE-RELATED DISTRESS

The key to recognizing distress suggestive of slope instability is the pattern of the distress. Detailed mapping of the character, location, magnitude, and extent of cracking is needed to evaluate whether a pattern exists. The pattern of the cracking may be of greater significance than the magnitude of one crack. Random cracking may be the result of typical performance of wood frame and stucco construction. Distress concentration and a pattern of frequency and magnitude may suggest unusual movement of the structure.

Distress due to landslides

The lateral or downward movement of landslides commonly results in apparent settlement of a structure. When the scarp of the landslide occurs within the structure, a relatively sharp change in the amount of settlement often occurs near the scarp (Fig. 2). In addition, the presence of wall or ceiling separations within the settlement area can indicate a landslide origin.

When the structure is within the limits of a large regional landslide, distress to the structure will often not suggest a landslide origin. Distortion and irregularities can be more subtle and can appear to be related to minor settlement. Significant cracking may not develop. Differential movement between the cut and fill portion of a building site can be rejuvenated, leading the investigator to diagnose the cause of the distress as fill settlement.

Minor cracking around doors and windows may increase in magnitude and frequency in one area of the home, for example, near the top of a descending slope. Distorted door and window openings may be deflected in a consistent direction. Ceiling

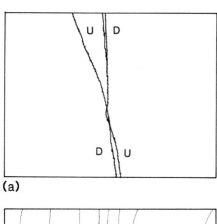

(a)

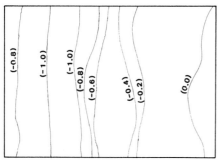

(b)

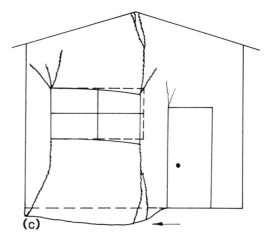

(c)

(a) CRACKING EXHIBITS EXTENSION AND DIFFERENTIAL MOVEMENT IN AREA OF SLIDE SCARP.

(b) RAPID FLOOR ELEVATION CHANGE IN AREA OF SCARP WITH RELATIVE MINOR IRREGULARITY AWAY FROM SCARP.

(c) OPEN CRACKS DISRUPTING RESIDENCE WALL. DISTORTED OPENINGS IN AREA OF SCARP.

Figure 2. Abnormal cracking and irregularities associated with development of a landslide across the structure.

beams and roof joints may consistently be separated in one direction. Measurable cracks that affect adjacent and contiguous walls and ceilings may be continuous across a part of the residence. All of these suggest a pattern of distress possibly related to slope instability.

Distress due to other soil related movements

Soil-related processes can cause distress similar in appearance to major slope movement, complicating recognition of a hazard. Types of soil movement that can distress residential developments include alternate expansion and shrinkage of earth materials, fill settlement, and differential movement between cut and fill.

Changes in moisture content result in volume changes in expansive soil, which can distress rigid improvements. Moisture changes can occur due to over or under irrigation, rainfall, poor drainage control, and leaking utility lines. The house sewer line should not be overlooked as a possible source of increased moisture caused by leaking. Movement due to expansive soil can cause significant cracking and irregularity in structures, especially when the expansiveness of the soil is not considered in the foundation design. Unreinforced slabs and wood floors supported on isolated pier footings tend to be the most vulnerable. Doming of floors and lifting of lighter portions of the structure are common distress patterns suggestive of expansive soil-related distress (Fig. 3).

Differential settlement can cause distress patterns similar to slope instability (Fig. 4). Deeper fill sections will consolidate more than shallow fills. Improvements that cross variably thick fill will undergo irregularities due to normal, anticipated differential settlement. Distress patterns can be similar to slope instability where the thicker fill deposits exist near the top of slopes. Careful attention to distress patterns and their correlation with fill thickness is needed to differentiate settlement from slope instability. Differential settlement between different earth materials can also cause cracking and irregularity of improvements, which can be misinterpreted to be slope instability.

EXPLORATION TECHNIQUES AND LIMITATIONS

Subsurface exploration is critical to the determination of the type and mechanics of slope instability. Property-line limitations, physical site constraints, high costs, and reluctant neighbors hamper site and neighborhood reconnaissance. Conventional exploration techniques are aided by modern instrumentation and detailed site monitoring.

Site reconnaissance

The initial visit should include careful observation of the site and neighborhood conditions. The condition of the street and surrounding improvements should be noted because they may suggest a pattern and give a clue to the causes and extent of the distress under investigation. Cracking in streets and sidewalks can

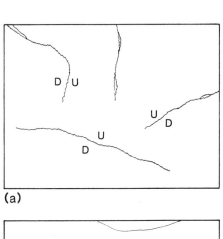

(a)

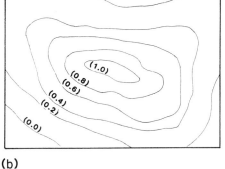

(b)

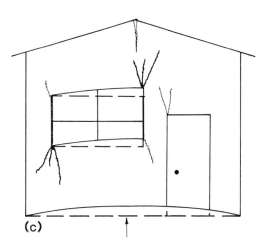

(c)

(a) CRACKING RADIATES AWAY FROM DOMED AREA.

(b) OBVIOUS DOMING CONCENTRATED IN AREA OF CRACKING. DIFFERENTIAL ELEVATION GREATER THAN 3/4'' (19 mm).

(c) IRREGULAR WINDOW AND DOOR OPENINGS AND PATTERN OF CRACKING WITH CRACK WIDTH GREATER THAN 1/16'' (1.6 mm).

Figure 3. Abnormal cracking and irregularities suggestive of expansive soil heaving.

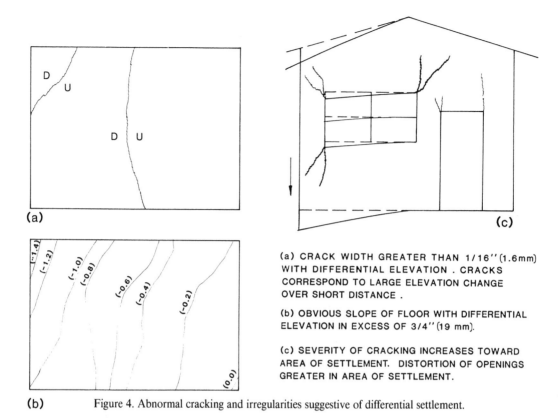

(a) CRACK WIDTH GREATER THAN 1/16" (1.6mm)
WITH DIFFERENTIAL ELEVATION . CRACKS
CORRESPOND TO LARGE ELEVATION CHANGE
OVER SHORT DISTANCE .

(b) OBVIOUS SLOPE OF FLOOR WITH DIFFERENTIAL
ELEVATION IN EXCESS OF 3/4" (19 mm).

(c) SEVERITY OF CRACKING INCREASES TOWARD
AREA OF SETTLEMENT. DISTORTION OF OPENINGS
GREATER IN AREA OF SETTLEMENT.

Figure 4. Abnormal cracking and irregularities suggestive of differential settlement.

be the result of settlement of utility-line backfill, differential settlement between cut and fill, and/or the effects of expansive soil. Unfortunately, initial movement of large regional landslides has often resulted in distress of graded streets and pads along the cut and fill contacts, leading early investigators to assume that cracking was related to grading, and not to regional instability.

Attention should be paid to adjacent developments. Ongoing repairs or exterior distress similar to that on the site being investigated may suggest a regional problem. Unfortunately, neighbors are generally reluctant to discuss problems about their homes. People do not like to acknowledge that their home may be unstable. Cracking may have been ignored in the hope that it is not significant. In addition, information provided by neighbors on neighborhood problems may not be accurate, and must be verified.

The residence and surrounding grounds should be carefully viewed and distress categorized in detail. Comparison between initial observations and conditions at a later date can be useful to distinguish the character and magnitude of movement. Changes in the width and pattern of cracking can serve as an initial monitoring tool. However, stress release within a structure after movement has stopped can result in enlargement of distress, giving the false impression of continued movement.

Distress of free-standing garden walls perpendicular to slopes can be a good indicator of slope movement. Construction and reinforcement of these walls is generally poor, and distress can indicate yielding and movement of the slope. The pattern of cracking on exterior slabs and walks can also be a clue to the cause of the distress.

Evaluating the relative elevation of the residence floor is very useful. A floor level survey can be quickly and economically performed using a water level or manometer. Two interconnected columns of water will seek the same level, regardless of the distance between the columns. Using this principle, one water column is placed at a fixed location and serves as the zero point or datum. The other column is provided with a measuring scale to calibrate differences in elevation from the datum. The scaled water column is moved throughout the house and the difference in elevation relative to the datum is recorded. Readings are taken at frequent intervals and data points are contoured. The interpretation of the results is useful in evaluating the cause of the cracking and can also aid the investigator in establishing whether unusual irregularities exist (Figs. 1–4). Manometer readings should be carefully recorded on a systematic grid if possible. This will allow the survey to be duplicated at a later date as part of a monitoring program.

Subsurface exploration

Adequate subsurface exploration is imperative, but is generally limited by economic and physical constraints. Property lines limit the area available for exploration, which may not allow adequate exploration of the postulated instability. Neighbors are rarely willing to allow subsurface exploration on their property to evaluate a possible landslide that they do not want to exist.

Existing improvements limit the open space available for drill-rig access. Often the cost of preparing a site for drill-rig access and clean up after drilling exceeds the cost of the exploratory boring. The homeowner must support the exploration, because it is impossible to return a property to preexploration condition. Limited access generally requires the use of portable drilling equipment. Small equipment has lower power and drilling capability, which makes a deep boring costly, time consuming, and sometimes impossible.

When possible, a portable drill rig can be supplemented with a full-size drill rig where access is better. However, access is generally only available away from the top of the slope and the potential problem area. The full-size rig is able to advance a deep boring at a more economical rate and can provide detailed information to be correlated with the limited data obtained from the portable drill holes.

Hand labor can be effective when used in combination with drilling equipment. Hand labor can be used to verify the depth of foundations, and to excavate test holes on the inside of structures and on the slope face. The information is then correlated with data from the deep borings. Hand labor can be cost effective if exploratory excavations are to be limited to 4.6 to 6.1 m (15 to 20 ft.

Exploration by instrumentation

Exploration time can be minimized when exploring an area of active movement by beginning the program with instrumentation. Slope indicators and tiltmeters are widely employed, easy to use methods of instrumentation that can be effective in defining the depth, areal extent, and rate of movement. This information is imperative for selection of a stabilization method. Data from the early monitoring can be correlated with drill-hole data to define the causes of the movement and remove the inconsistencies of subjective interpretation of bore-hole data from the evaluation.

Need for assumptions

Any evaluation will require assumptions. Limited data resulting from monetary and time limitations make this a reality. Unfortunately, those using your evaluation want absolutes. The insurance adjustor, the attorney, and the homeowner do not want "maybe" and "appears to be," but these cannot be eliminated during the exploration phase. Continued monitoring during the project will help eliminate some of the assumptions.

Importance of monitoring

Monitoring from recognition through stabilization helps to verify the causes of instability, the design scheme, and the success of the treatment. Establishing a monitoring base should be done as early in the investigation as possible. Monitoring can be accomplished with techniques as simple as accurate crack mapping and manometer readings. More detailed monitoring can include instrumentation with tiltmeters and slope indicators. All forms of monitoring should be utilized if possible.

Monitoring should be performed throughout data evalua-

tion, preparation of stabilization plans, and implementation of the stabilization program. Continued involvement in the property increases the geotechnical investigator's confidence with hypothesized causes of the movement, which are fundamental to establishing site stability. Changed physical conditions should be recognized and incorporated into the analysis to provide the most effective and site-specific stabilization approach. Monitoring after stabilization helps assure the stabilization method is successful.

SELECTION OF A REASONABLE REMEDIAL TREATMENT

Selection of a reasonable repair method and stabilization devices depends on the limits of the failing mass and whether instability is associated with failure along a predetermined defect or through an inherently weak mass. Easy-to-use computer programs can aid in the evaluation of the most critical failure surface and in the design of the repair. The investigator must be aware of the limitations of soil sampling and laboratory testing techniques. These limitations must be accounted for by including an adequate factor of safety in the final design. When a good understanding of the slide geometry is present, the back-calculated strengths should be used over the laboratory strengths.

What is a reasonable remedial treatment?

The homeowner is not served by a time-consuming exploration program that does not result in a conclusion; nor are they served by a hasty, poorly thought out stabilization approach. Repairs are effective if the factor of safety is sufficiently increased by common and economical construction techniques in a timely manner.

A reasonable remedial treatment is a repair approach that can and would be implemented by a homeowner to improve the stability of the property. A reasonable repair includes stabilization of the site with a sufficient factor of safety to improve the condition over which present exists and eliminate a hazardous condition. The repair approach should consider the age and economic life of the improvement to be repaired. However, these elements are secondary in importance to eliminating a hazard. Typically, it is not possible to completely eliminate the risk to the property or eliminate slope instability on and around the site. Possible diminution of property value is not a hazard and should not be considered in selecting a repair approach. The temptation is to recommend a system that is designed to resist all possible scenarios and has a high factor of safety to allow for the occurrence of unanticipated events. However, those types of repairs are rarely implemented due to the cost and difficulty of construction. Major foundation underpinning and site regrading may not be reasonable remedial treatments if a hazard does not exist and if the treatment is intended to upgrade the site to modern standards for the purposes of maintaining the resale value of the property.

Any repair approach should utilize conventional construction techniques that can be implemented with the least difficulty. Mass grading is cost effective, but can rarely be utilized due to constraints imposed by existing improvements. Soldier piles are used where physical constraints limit grading to stabilize the failing mass. Pile design analysis requires knowledge of the variation in strength parameters within the mass. sher pins can be effectively used when failure is occurring in a strong mass along a weak, well-defined failure plane. Shear pins are more economical than soldier piles because they are designed to resist movement only along the weak bed. The slope gradient can be lowered through the use of retaining walls, and a more stable condition can be created. Dewatering is crucial to the design scheme and the anticipated life of the system. Maintenance requirements for all elements of the repair are important considerations. Increasing the density of the soil by grouting can reduce, but not eliminate, the potential for future settlement. Grouting can be successful in hillside areas when used in combination with soldier piles, which retain the grout and soil.

CONCLUSIONS

Single-family residential construction is not a perfect process. cracking and irregularities occur with all forms of construction due to typical performance of building materials, the degree of care used by the builder, normal deterioration, and soil movement. Wood shrinkage can be significant and can result in apparent settlement, gaps, and irregularities that are interpreted by owners to indicate foundation and land movement. Concrete products shrink during curing, causing cracking that cannot be eliminated. Slab doming, depressions, slopes, and cracks are common, and can be misinterpreted as indications of soil movement. Normal plaster and stucco cracks radiate off the corners of window and door openings. Normal settlement of a structure, movement due to changes in the live load or the wind load, or adjustments of the structure due to subtle soil movements tend to widen and lengthen the cosmetic cracking common to all wood-frame and stucco construction. Successful identification of slope instability requires the geotechnical professional to differentiate typical construction performance from cracking and irregularities due to slope movement.

The character, pattern, and magnitude of the cracking must be carefully observed because they are key to recognizing distress suggestive of slope instability. Distress concentration and a regular pattern of frequency and magnitude may suggest unusual movement of the structure. Distress of a residence affected by the early stages of large regional landslide movement can be more subtle and can appear to be related to minor settlement. Differential movement between the cut and fill portions of a building site can be rejuvenated, leading the investigator to misdiagnose the cause of the distress. Alternate expansion and shrinkage of earth materials, fill settlement, and differential movement between cut and fill can cause distress similar in appearance to major slope movement, which complicates recognition of a hazard. Distress can be misinterpreted to be caused by slope instability.

Initial site observations should include careful observation of the site and neighborhood conditions. Comparison between initial observations and later conditions can help distinguish the character and magnitude of movement. Monitoring changes in crack width and pattern is useful, but stress release within a structure after movement has stopped can result in enlargement of distress, giving the false impression of continued movement. The relative elevation of the residence floor can be quickly and economically determined with a manometer. Data are useful in evaluating the cause of the cracking and establishing whether unusual irregularities exist. Manometer readings can be economically incorporated into the monitoring program.

Subsurface exploration is critical to the determination of the type and mechanics of slope instability, but is generally limited by economic and physical constraints. Property-line limits may not allow adequate exploration. Exploration should incorporate full-size drilling equipment, portable equipment, and hand labor to obtain the maximum subsurface data. Instrumentation can be effective in defining the depth, areal extent, and rate of movement, which must be known before recommending a stabilization method. Limited data, resulting from monetary and time constraints, require that assumptions be entered into the analysis, despite the desire for absolutes by those using the data.

Monitoring throughout all stages of the project, from the initial site visit to the final stabilization program, should be performed. The results increase the geotechnical investigator's confidence with hypothesized causes of the movement. Monitoring allows changed physical conditions to be recognized and incorporated into the analysis and the stabilization approach. Monitoring after stabilization helps assure that the selected stabilization method is successful.

Stabilization recommendations depend on the limits of the failing mass and whether failure is occurring along a predetermined defect or through an inherently weak mass. The limitations of soil sampling and laboratory testing techniques must be accounted for by including an adequate factor of safety into the final design.

The public is not served by a time-consuming, inconclusive exploration or by a hasty, poorly thought out stabilization approach. A reasonable remedial treatment is one that (1) can and would be implemented by a homeowner; (2) uses economical construction techniques in a timely manner; and (3) stabilizes the site with a sufficient factor of safety to improve the condition over that which presently exists and eliminates a hazardous condition.

The identification of subtle residential distress presents a challenging problem for the geotechnical professional. Only careful examination and considerable experience will permit the differentiation between normal construction-related distress from that caused by instability. There is no substitute for detailed observation. Consultants must constantly be aware and informed about construction techniques and common shortfalls. Occasional observation of new residences under construction and connection with experienced contractors is as important as keeping abreast of new techniques in landslide investigation.

MANUSCRIPT ACCEPTED BY THE SOCIETY FEBRUARY 12, 1992

Geological Society of America
Reviews in Engineering Geology, Volume IX
1992

Chapter 5

The Mameyes, Puerto Rico, landslide disaster of October 7, 1985

Randall W. Jibson
U.S. Geological Survey, Box 25046, MS 966, Denver Federal Center, Denver, Colorado 80225

ABSTRACT

From October 5–8, 1985, a tropical wave centered about 25 km northeast of Ponce, Puerto Rico, produced as much as 560 mm of rainfall in 24 hours and as much as 70 mm in one hour. This extraordinarily heavy rainfall triggered a rock-block slide that destroyed much of the Mameyes residential area, on the northwest outskirts of Ponce.

The Mameyes landslide failed in three distinct phases between 3:00 and 4:00 a.m. (local time) on October 7, 1985. The first two phases of sliding involved translational sliding of two 12-m-thick slabs of calcareous-sandstone bedrock along bedding-plane surfaces parallel to the slope surface. The third phase of sliding involved the toppling failure of a block that disaggregated and formed a rock fall on the western part of the slide. Subsidiary flow failures onto the toe and from the downstream face of the toe were triggered by the heavy rainfall and the rupture of a water pipe that emptied as much as 4 million liters of water onto the slide.

The Mameyes landslide is approximately triangular in plan view; the maximum width and length are both about 250 m. The total area of the landslide is ~35,000 m^2, and the slab of bedrock and soil that failed is about 12 m thick and comprises ~300,000 m^3. The landslide moved downslope 30 m, parallel to the 17°–24° bedrock dip. At most, an estimated 120 homes were destroyed by the landslide, and at least 129 people were killed, though only 39 bodies were recovered. This death toll is the largest from a single landslide in North American history.

Calculations of the prelandslide slope stability at the site indicate that when the water table was below the potential shear surface, the factor of safety against failure was about 1.26. A water table about 6 m above the shear surface, which would saturate half the thickness of the slide block, reduces the factor of safety to 1.0. A water table at this level is a reasonable result of the conditions preceding failure.

The landslide area has been stabilized by engineering measures and was developed as a memorial park to the landslide victims.

INTRODUCTION

On October 5–8, 1985, a tropical wave, which later developed into tropical storm Isabel, produced extraordinary rainfalls on the island of Puerto Rico. At some places, 24 hour rainfall exceeded 560 mm, which approaches the record 24 hour rainfall in Puerto Rico of 585 mm during the San Ciriaco Hurricane of 1899 (Federal Emergency Management Agency, 1985). The October 1985 storm was centered over the central southern coast, where the intense rainfall caused severe flooding and landsliding. During the most intense rainfall, early in the morning of October

7, a rock-block slide destroyed much of the Mameyes residential area, on the northwest outskirts of Ponce (Fig. 1). At least 129 people were killed by the landslide; this is the largest death toll from any single landslide in North American history.

Campbell and others (1985) and Jibson (1986) documented the hazards resulting from the landslide at Mameyes, and Campbell and others (1986) briefly described the landslide. This chapter provides a more extensive description and documentation and includes discussions of (1) the physical setting of the Mameyes area; (2) the October 1985 storm that triggered the landslide; (3) the occurrence and morphology of the landslide, including

Jibson, R. W., 1992, The Mameyes, Puerto Rico, landslide disaster of October 7, 1985, *in* Slosson, J. E., Keene, A. G., and Johnson, J. A., eds., Landslides/Landslide Mitigation: Boulder, Colorado, Geological Society of America Reviews in Engineering Geology, v. IX.

Figure 1. Oblique aerial photograph showing the Mameyes landslide. The lighter areas are severely disrupted parts of the landslide; the dark, vegetated areas in the center of the landslide are more intact slide blocks. View is to northwest.

eyewitness accounts and damage estimates; (4) the stability of the slope before the landslide; and (5) the remedial measures taken to stabilize the landslide.

PHYSICAL SETTING

Geology and physiography

The Mameyes residential area is situated on the northwest outskirts of the city of Ponce on the south-central coast of Puerto Rico (Fig. 2). The area lies in an east-west–trending belt of sedimentary rocks, primarily limestones, with lesser amounts of sandstones, claystones, and conglomerates, that separates the interior mountainous part of the island from the relatively flat coastal plain.

The hillside that failed at Mameyes is composed of the calcareous unit of the Oligocene and Miocene Juana Diaz Formation (Maury, 1929; Monroe, 1973), which consists of lenses of calcareous sandstone between interbeds of weaker silt and clay, overlain by chalk and chalky limestone. The limestone beds are overlain in most places by a mantle of caliche, a meter or more thick, that is slightly indurated. In the vicinity of Mameyes, the Juana Diaz Formation strikes approximately east-west and dips 17°–24° to the south (Fig. 2). The hill on which Mameyes is

situated is nearly conical, having slopes of 14°–25° and a total relief of about 80 m. The southern part of this hillside, that which failed, thus forms a dip slope. On this southern exposure of the hillside, the strike of the bedrock roughly parallels the contours of the hill, so that the dip is slightly west of south on the western part of the southern exposure, and is east of south on the eastern part (Fig. 2).

The bedrock exposed in the landslide scarp contains at least three approximately orthogonal joint sets, two nearly vertical and one along bedding. Joint orientation changes somewhat along the scarp; average orientations are N65°W, 80°S, N40°E, 90°, and N85°E, 25°S. Joint spacing is generally 10–50 cm. Many of the joints exposed in the scarp are open to a depth of at least 10 m and show evidence of downward percolation of ground water, but no open joints extend to the ground surface. Discontinuous blocks of surficial soils buried in filled joints suggest that previous landslide movement created open joints that extended to the ground surface at one time.

A stream channel extends along the base of the southern slope. This channel has incised the base of the slope, so that the lowermost 10–20 m of the slope is steeper (25°–30°) than the slope above. This incision and steepening of the lower slope probably exposed bedding-plane surfaces and facilitated block sliding.

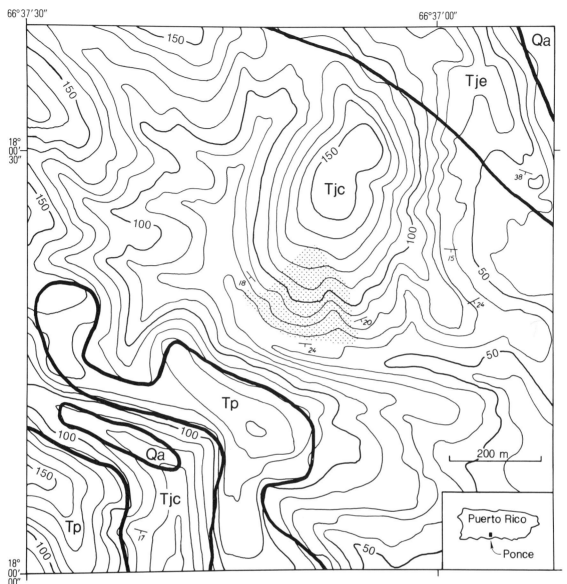

Figure 2. Map showing topography and geology in the vicinity of the Mameyes landslide. Landslide site is shaded; heavy lines denote geologic contacts; contour interval is 10 m; datum is mean sea level. Geologic units shown are from Krushensky and Monroe (1975); from oldest to youngest they are as follows: Tje, detrital unit of the Juana Diaz Formation (Oligocene and Miocene); Tjc, calcareous unit of the Juana Diaz Formation; Tp, Ponce Limestone (Miocene); Qa, Quaternary alluvium.

Climate

The south-central coast of Puerto Rico normally receives about 1000 mm of rainfall annually, most of which falls between May and October, the hurricane season (Monroe, 1980). Rainfall tends to occur in sudden showers lasting only 15–30 min and producing 15 mm or more of rainfall, which generates large amounts of runoff. The mean maximum temperature is 30 °C and the mean minimum is 21 °C. This warm, humid climate,

prone to intense cloudbursts, results in rapid, deep weathering of surficial materials and the formation of steep-sided, deeply incised valleys (Monroe, 1980).

STORM OF OCTOBER 5–8, 1985

The storm of October 5–8, 1985, was described by the U.S. Geological Survey (1985) and by Jibson (1986). Peak rainfalls were centered about 25 km northeast of Ponce, and the entire

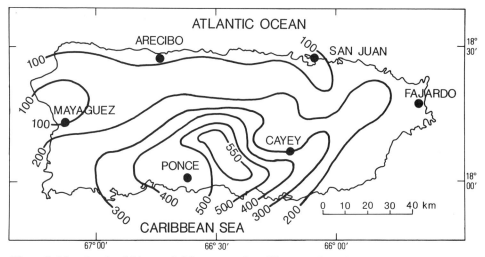

Figure 3. Map showing 24 hour rainfall amounts (in millimeters) throughout Puerto Rico from 8:00 a.m. (local time) October 6, to 8:00 a.m. October 7, 1985 (after U.S. Geological Survey, 1985). Isohyet intervals 50 or 100 mm.

south-central coast had storm totals exceeding 300 mm, most of which fell on October 7 (Fig. 3). At some locations along the southern coast, 24 hour rainfall totals exceeded maximum historical values. Rainfall intensities in some areas were greater than 70 mm/hr, an extreme amount. Several streams and rivers in southern Puerto Rico produced discharges that exceeded the maximum previously recorded, and the discharge at Rio Cerrillos, which flows through Ponce, exceeded the expected 100 year discharge. Rainfall in most areas reached peak intensity in the early morning hours of Monday, October 7.

Table 1 shows rainfall amounts for October 5–8 at the four National Weather Service rain gages nearest and closest in elevation to Mameyes. The average of the four-day storm totals is more than 540 mm, and 24 hour accumulations (for October 7) averaged almost 470 mm (National Oceanic and Atmospheric Administration, 1985). This indicates that the Ponce area received an amount of rainfall in 24 hours equal to almost half its annual average.

MAMEYES LANDSLIDE

Sequence of failure

The hillslide at Mameyes failed in three distinct phases. According to eyewitnesses (interviewed by D. G. Herd, U.S. Geological Survey; 1985, personal commun.), the first phase of movement began between 3:00 and 4:00 a.m. (local time) on Monday, October 7, 1985. The initial failure consisted of a slab of hillside bedrock, which probably covered an area larger than than 8,000 m^2, that slid more or less intact along relatively weak clay and silt layers exposed near the base of the slope. This slab pushed a large mass of disrupted material into the valley bottom and created a bulging toe (Fig. 4). After no more than 30 min, a second slab of hillside bedrock, about the same size as the first one, detached upslope from the first and slid in the same manner. The second block came to rest several meters upslope from the upper edge of the first block; the area between the blocks was covered by broken and disrupted bedrock (Fig. 5). Within a few

TABLE 1. PRECIPITATION AMOUNTS NEAR MAMEYES FROM OCTOBER 5 THROUGH 8, 1985

Station	Direction from Mameyes (°)	Distance from Mameyes (km)	Storm Precipitation* October 5 (mm)	October 6 (mm)	October 7 (mm)	October 8 (mm)	Storm Total (mm)
Corral Viejo	N35W	5	10.6	9.7	403.9	25.6	449.8
Juana Diaz	N80E	13	0.0	0.0	564.7	76.7	641.4
Penuelas	N70W	11	12.7	18.3	436.9	45.7	513.6
Ponce 4E	S85E	9	13.2	19.1	462.4	66.3	560.8

*Data from National Oceanic and Atmospheric Administration (1985).

Figure 4. Oblique aerial photograph of the landslide toe. Note the convex upward profile and the runup onto the opposing valley face. View is to west.

Figure 5. Photograph of area between first and second main slide blocks. Enough disrupted material was present to prevent the intact blocks from coming to rest in contact with each other. The house in the center of the photograph was astride a tensile fracture that opened and dropped the house, intact, on its side. The line indicates the contact of the first slide block (above the line) with the disrupted material; the second slide block is beyond the right edge of the photograph. View is to west.

minutes of the movement of the second block, a third block, on the western margin of the landslide, detached and began to slide. After only a few meters of movement, the block toppled forward, disaggregated, and formed a rock fall.

Landslide characteristics and features

Figure 6 is a map of the Mameyes landslide. The map was prepared from two air photographs that were not orthogonally rectified, so some distortion of shapes and sizes may be present,

but general dimensions and relative positions of features are well represented. The maximum width and length of the landslide are both about 250 m, and the total area of the slide is about 35,000 m². The area of the original hillside that detached and failed probably covered about 25,000 m². Field observations and drilling data indicate that the shear surface is about 12 m deep, thus, the total volume of displaced material is about 300,000 m³. Displacement of a water pipe extending across the second main slide block, which may have been leaking before the slide, indicates downslope movement of about 30 m parallel to the dip of the bedrock.

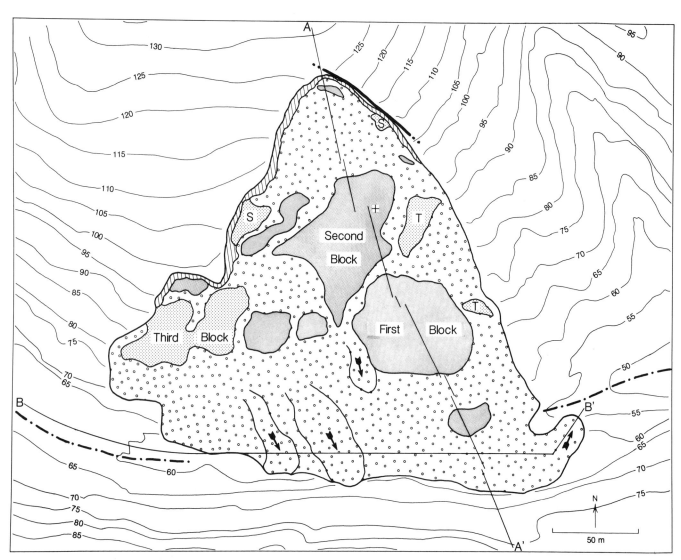

Figure 6. Map of the Mameyes landslide. Heavy solid line denotes landslide boundary; hachured area is scarp; dark gray tint denotes intact blocks that translated with no rotation; light gray tint denotes partially disrupted blocks that toppled (T) or slumped (S); arrows denote flows of disrupted landslide material; small open-circle pattern denotes areas of severely jumbled and disaggregated bedrock and soil. The heavy dash-dot line is the stream channel. Along the east part of the head scarp, the line shown dotted at the ends is the trace of a fault illustrated in Figure 12. Profile A-A′ is shown in Figure 17 and profile B-B′ is shown in Figure 18. The cross indicates the location of the drill hole described in Figure 16. Contour interval 5 m; datum is mean sea level (contours scaled from map of Mameyes area prepared by Puerto Rico Highway Authority in November 1985, original scale 1:500).

The upper margin of the landslide coincides closely with the upper limit of development of the Mameyes neighborhood, so that most of the landslide area was covered by dense housing. All of these houses emptied domestic sewage into cesspools, which probably raised the ground-water level in the underlying hillside.

The main slide blocks appear as islands surrounded by large areas of more highly disrupted and mixed rock and soil fragments. As the main blocks began to move, their margins probably shattered and disasggregated through interaction with the slide margin and adjacent blocks; the jointed bedrock probably facilitated disaggregation along the edges of the blocks. The relatively intact blocks show moderate to severe ground cracking (Fig. 7), and buildings on these blocks, though not disintegrated as were those on more disrupted parts of the slide, were wracked, severely cracked, and uninhabitable. In addition to the main slide blocks, several smaller subsidiary blocks, some intact and some partly disrupted, moved by toppling (forward rotational movement) or slumping (backward rotational movement). Some of these failed from the newly created headwall and lateral scarps; others failed from the edges of the main slide blocks.

The headwall scarp and much of the western margin of the slide consist of a vertical to overhanging face as high as 10 m. The margin to the west of the crown formed along a preexisting joint surface (Fig. 8) that shows evidence of long-term ground-water penetration along joint surfaces and shearing either from deep-seated faulting or past, near-surface slope movement (Fig. 9). Exposures of disrupted bedding in the joint face, about 100 m downslope from the crown, indicate previous movement of the slope at Mameyes (Fig. 10). The shape and orientation of this area of disturbed bedding suggests that a slab of bedrock on the hillside detached and moved a meter or more downslope, which created an open fissure in the ground surface that was later filled by adjacent hillside material. An undisturbed, well-developed soil horizon that is continuous from adjacent, undisturbed parts of the hillside across the top of this feature indicates that the fissure probably formed and was filled hundreds or thousands of years ago. Because the disturbed zone passes through the present scarp, the previous landslide movement probably extended farther to the west than the present landslide.

The margin to the east of the crown has a lower, less extensive scarp than that on the west (Fig. 11). The eastern margin is defined by a fault-breccia zone of very weak, disrupted material. The fault is well exposed at the crown of the landslide (Fig. 6), where beds exhibit drag that indicates a relative downward component of dip slip of the units east of the fault. Beds on either side of the fault display discordant bedding (Fig. 12). The fault-breccia zone extends along the scarp southeastward from the crown almost to the limit of the scarp. Thus, the upper margins of this landslide, both east and west of the crown, formed along preexisting discontinuities.

The lower parts of both slide margins are less well defined than the upper parts and are characterized by ground cracks that decrease in size and number downslope.

The disrupted parts of the landslide (Fig. 6) are covered by a mass of broken bedrock blocks as large as several cubic meters (Fig. 13). On the lower parts of the slide, these disrupted areas also contain abundant house debris and scattered personal belongings, because the ground disruption was severe enough to

Figure 7. Photograph showing cracks in ground surface on second main landslide block.

Figure 8. Photograph showing overhanging joint surface along upper west margin of the landslide. Close-up photograph of this joint surface is shown in Figure 9.

Figure 9. Close-up photograph of joint surface shown in Figure 8. Note the stained striations indicating movement along the joint surface prior to the October 1985 landslide. Previous movement may have been related to faulting or to movement of a landslide from right to left. Rock hammer in upper center shows scale.

Figure 10. Photograph of disrupted bedding (between solid lines) on western margin of the landslide. This feature probably resulted from a small amount of landslide movement that opened a ground crack that subsequently filled with adjacent material. The undisturbed soil horizon extending across this feature (dashed line) indicates that it is several hundreds or thousands of years old. Width of filled fracture (between vertical lines) is about 2 m.

Figure 11. Photograph of striated surface along the relatively low east margin of the landslide.

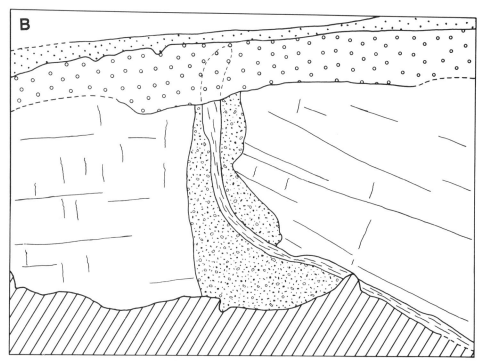

Figure 12. A: Photograph showing drag along a fault, shown in Figure 6, exposed at the crown of the landslide. B: Diagram of features shown in photograph. Dot pattern denotes modern solum; open-circle pattern denotes caliche mantle; rubble pattern denotes fault-breccia zone, which is about 1.5 m wide at its top; hachured area is covered. Gently dipping lines on either side of the fault zone indicate bedding planes in intact bedrock, which are discordant across the fault. Shorter lines orthogonal to the bedding indicate prominent joints. Drag along the fault curved the bed shown by offset dashed lines upward.

Figure 13. Photograph of disrupted area (below and right of the dashed line) between second main slide block (above the dashed line) and landslide crown. View is to southwest.

disintegrate overlying structures (Fig. 14). A few houses were swept and pushed downslope intact and came to rest in a helter-skelter arrangement (Fig. 15). Lobate, convex-upward masses of blocks and debris on the lower parts of the slide suggest that flowage of disrupted material occurred, both on the slide mass and from the downstream face of the toe.

Drilling (conducted by Ponce I & M Engineering Laboratory, Inc.) indicates that the shear surface is about 12 m deep, at the contact between the upper, sandy and silty part of the calcareous unit of the Juana Diaz Formation and the lower, limestone part of the unit. Figure 16 shows a drill log of a boring on the landslide (location shown in Figs. 6 and 17) and includes material descriptions, standard penetration test (SPT) blow counts, and index properties; SPT blow counts and index properties were not measured below about 14 m, the level of the limestone part of the formation. The layer of clayey silt at a depth of about 12 m probably is the layer that failed. This material has the lowest SPT blow count, the greatest plasticity index, and second-highest water content, which at this depth passes into the plastic range. A shear surface 12 m deep is consistent with the geometry of the landslide as observed in the field. Figure 17 is a longitudinal profile down the landslide (profile location shown in Fig. 6). Because much of the slope face was parallel to the bedrock dip, the upper surfaces of intact landslide blocks came to rest near the original ground-surface level. Past fluvial incision at the base of the slope had exposed the potential shear surface and facilitated planar block sliding. The basal shear surface is nowhere exposed,

though in places it is likely buried by only a few meters of disrupted material. The bulging toe formed as the slide blocks pushed a large amount of disrupted material up the opposing slope and as the first slide block was thrust beneath the toe material and uplifted the surface of the toe (Fig. 4).

Figure 18 shows a transverse profile across the toe of the landslide (profile location shown in Fig. 6). This profile extends along the top of a uniformly sloping box culvert, across the toe, and back down to the box culvert. Interpolation of the culvert beneath the landslide indicates that the toe is almost 15 m thick beneath its highest point. The steep, downstream face of the toe (Fig. 18, right side of profile) underwent flow failure after the main landslide movement. Surface and subsurface drainage from both the rainfall and water introduced from a ruptured water pipe were concentrated at this face.

After the major landslide movement, the Mamayes landslide and adjacent areas remained significant landslide hazards. The vertical to overhanging scarp and margins of the slide continued to retreat as large and small blocks fell, toppled, and slid from the scarp onto the upper parts of the landslide. The detached block and rock-slide area on the western part of the landslide remained only marginally stable and was susceptible to further movement if subjected to heavy rains or careless construction practices at the base of the slope. Hillsides adjacent to the scarps along the east and west margins of the slide were also marginally stable. The disrupted material at the toe of the landslide dried and hardened within several days after the rain ceased, but if saturated by heavy

R. W. Jibson

Figure 14. Photograph of disrupted area above toe of landslide. Note the house debris and personal belongings scattered on the surface. View is to north.

Figure 15. Photograph of houses near toe of landslide that were pushed downslope and deposited in a helter-skelter arrangement. View is to southeast.

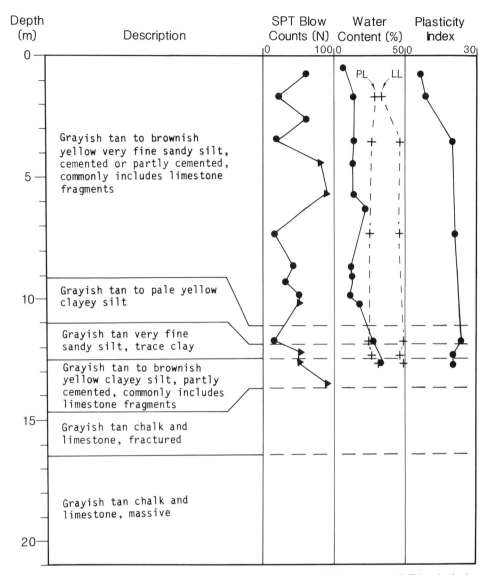

Figure 16. Log of drill hole on Mameyes landslide. Location shown in Figures 6 and 17. Triangles in the standard penetration test (SPT) blow counts indicate that the sampler was not driven the full 30 cm. Crosses in the water-content data indicate liquid and plastic limits (right and left crosses, respectively); area between dashed lines denotes range of water contents in which the material behaves plastically.

rains, this material could undergo flow failure and endanger areas downstream.

Factors contributing to slope failure

The October 5–8 storm undoubtedly triggered the Mameyes landslide. Figure 19 shows cumulative rainfall from the storm plotted against time for a continuously recording rain gage about 11 km west-southwest of Mameyes. The occurrence of the land-slide near the end of the most intense rainfall (about 70 mm/hr) and at the peak of the cumulative curve shows the causal relation between the storm and the slope failure, although the relative

importance of rainfall intensity and total cumulative rainfall in the triggering of the landslide is unclear. The timing of the slide suggests that a storm having slightly less intensity and (or) total rainfall might not have triggered slope failure.

Several factors in addition to the storm probably contributed to slope failure.

1. The geologic structure and topography interacted to provide the geometry conducive to block sliding, and the preexisting faults and joints influenced the ultimate shape and extent of the slide.

2. The landslide occurred near the end of Puerto Rico's rainy season, which normally is from May through October, and

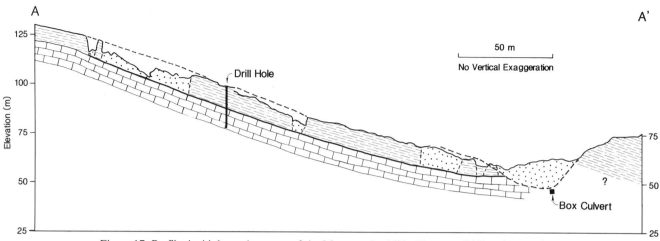

Figure 17. Profile A–A′ down the center of the Mameyes landslide. Heavy, solid line denotes shear surface; dashed line indicates estimated prelandslide ground surface; broken parallel line pattern indicates calcareous sand and silt of the Juana Diaz Formation; offset block pattern denotes limestone of the Juana Diaz Formation; dot pattern indicates disrupted landslide material. Location of the profile indicated in Figure 6.

Figure 18. Profile B–B′ across the toe of the Mameyes landslide. Hachured line, dashed where interpolated, denotes the box culvert. Location of profile shown in Figure 6. Dot pattern denotes disrupted landslide material.

the ground water was probably near its highest seasonal level. Rainfall near Mameyes from May 1 to October 4, 1985, was about 25 mm (5%) below normal; in the week preceding the landslide, total rainfall was about 7 mm, which is 22 mm below the estimated normal one-week rainfall for that period (National Oceanic and Atmospheric Administration, 1985). Thus, the Mameyes landslide took place near the end of a rainy season that was slightly drier than normal, and rainfall immediately preceding the storm certainly could not have produced abnormally high antecedent ground-water levels.

3. A 20 cm water pipe extended across the upper (second) slide block. Unsubstantiated reports suggest that this water pipe may have been leaking for several months before the slide, which could have significantly raised the ground-water level in the hillside and thus reduced the shear resistance. In addition, failure of the first block may have induced enough upslope deformation to have ruptured the water pipe, and the rapid introduction of a large amount of water may have then contributed to the failure of the second block. The ruptured pipe emptied a water tank having an estimated capacity of 4 million liters. This large amount of water, emptied onto the upper parts of the landslide, probably caused the flow of disrupted material, which was deposited in lobes on the toe. The infiltration from this water, along with the copious rainfall, probably also led to the flow failure of the downstream face of the toe.

4. Mameyes was a densely populated neighborhood, and all of the houses emptied domestic sewage into cesspools. This constant input of large amounts of water into the hillside probably resulted in a higher ground-water level there than at undeveloped hillsides having a similar geologic structure. That the upper margin of the slide coincides with the upper edge of development at Mameyes suggests that moisture introduced from cesspools contributed to the slope failure.

5. Steep cut slopes for roads, pathways, and houses near the base of the slope may have further destabilized the slope by exposing potential slip surfaces or removing basal support.

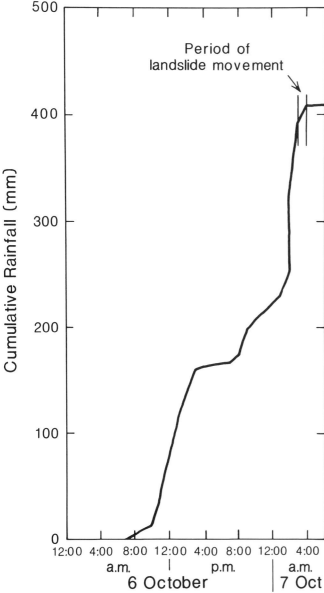

Figure 19. Graph of cumulative rainfall on October 6–7, 1985, near Tallaboa, 11 km west-southwest of Mameyes. The time of the landslide movement, between 3:00 and 4:00 a.m. (indicated by vertical lines), corresponds with the culmination of the highest intensity rainfall and the peak of the cumulative curve. Modified from U.S. Geological Survey (1985).

Damage and casualty estimates

An accurate inventory of the number of homes destroyed was impossible because most of the structures within the margins of the landslide were disintegrated, and the debris was scattered and mixed. In addition, Mameyes is a squatter community, and no official records of the number and locations of houses and inhabitants exist. The density of housing on the landslide, however, was similar to the housing density on adjacent slopes. Ap-

plying this density of about one home per 300 m² of ground surface yields an estimate of about 120 homes. This number may be greater than the actual number of homes destroyed, because the upper parts of landslide were less densely populated than the average.

A total of 39 bodies were recovered from the landslide before recovery efforts were suspended. The disaggregated landslide material, though very plastic when saturated, dried to form a very hard deposit, which made excavation for bodies ineffective. Therefore, the Puerto Rican government closed the site and suspended recovery operations. In addition to the 39 confirmed casualties, 90 persons were declared missing and presumed dead, to yield a total death toll of 129 persons. Since the time of the landslide, the Puerto Rican government has revised this death toll downward to reflect the number of legal actions initiated to have people officially declared dead; approximately 40 such requests have been filed. But Mameyes was a squatter community, and most of its population was indigent. Therefore, legal actions probably were initiated for only a portion of those missing and presumed dead.

I judge the figure of 129 to be a minimum death toll for several reasons. First, if only 100 homes were destroyed, a death toll of 129 would indicate that, on average, slightly more than one casualty resulted for every house that was destroyed. A figure of 1.29 casualties per destroyed house seems low, considering that (1) the landslide occurred in the middle of the night in a densely populated neighborhood consisting primarily of fairly large families; and (2) the large majority of houses destroyed were disintegrated beyond recognition. Also, the street at the base of the hill, which was inundated and buried by the landslide, contained several all-night bars that may have had several customers.

SLOPE STABILITY ANALYSIS

The landslide at Mameyes is well suited for analysis as an infinite slope. The basal shear surface is planar, and this surface probably was exposed near the base of the slope, so that little or no passive resistance was present at the downslope margin of the landslide. The headwall scarp and lateral margins of the slide formed along preexisting discontinuities, so little, if any, tensile resistance probably was present along these margins. The triangular shape, having the apex at the top of the slide, provided a geometry whereby the bedrock slabs could slide downslope freely. Thus, the rock-block slide at Mameyes is best modeled as a rigid friction block sliding on an inclined plane, whose factor of safety, in the absence of any pore-water pressure or cohesion, is

$$FS_d = \tan\phi'/\tan\alpha, \qquad (1)$$

where FS_d is the factor of safety in dry conditions, ϕ' is the effective friction angle of the material, and α is the angle from the horizontal to the shearing plane.

Samples obtained from borings on the landslide were tested in drained, direct shear by Ponce I & M Engineering Laboratory, Inc. (1986). Strength envelopes plotted from the data show that the material from the shear zone has no cohesion, a peak effective

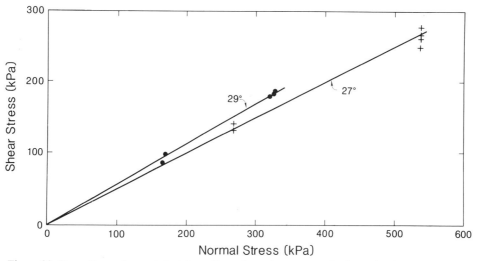

Figure 20. Strength envelopes plotted from direct-shear data on samples from the shear zone of the Mameyes landslide (data from Ponce I & M Engineering Laboratory, 1985). Dots indicate peak shear strengths; crosses indicate residual shear strengths.

friction angle of 29°, and a residual angle of 27° (Fig. 20). These values are reasonable for an uncemented clayey silt (Lambe and Whitman, 1969, p. 149). The angle of the shear plane is the dip angle of the hillside bedding, and ranges from 17°–24°. Therefore, in the absence of any pore-water pressure, the minimum factor of safety (ϕ' = 27°, α = 24°) against sliding is 1.14; the maximum factor of safety (ϕ' = 29°, α = 17°) is 1.81. The best estimates of the average conditions at the site (ϕ' = 27°, α = 22°) yield a factor of safety of 1.26. These calculations indicate that the hillside at Mameyes was stable when the water table was below the potential failure surface.

Campbell (1975, p. 19) showed that the factor of safety for a cohesionless infinite slope having ground-water flow parallel to the slope face can be expressed as

$$FS = [1 - (m\Gamma'/\Gamma)]\,(\tan\phi'/\tan\alpha). \qquad (2)$$

FS is the factor of safety, Γ' is the unit weight of water, Γ is the total unit weight of the material above the shear plane, and m is the proportion of the sliding block, measured vertically, that is saturated, such that when $m = 0$, the water table is at or below the shear plane, and when m = 1, the water table is at the ground surface.

For the condition of slope failure ($FS = 1$), combining equations 1 and 2 yields

$$m = (\Gamma/\Gamma')\,[1 - (1/FS_d)]. \qquad (3)$$

This expression allows calculation of the value of m required to reduce the factor of safety to 1.0, the onset of slope failure, if the factor of safety in dry conditions is known. Figure 21 is a plot of m as a function of FS_d, which shows the slope-failure condition for the range of unit weights appropriate for the landslide mate-

rials at Mameyes. For the best estimates of unit weight (23.6 kN/m^3) and FS_d (1.26), slope failure will occur when $m \geqslant 0.49$, or when slightly less than half the potential landslide block is below the water table. This means that for a landslide block 12 m thick (measured vertically), a water table 5.9 m above the shear surface will trigger slope failure. In jointed rock resting on less permeable material, a water table of this height generated by extreme rainfall, constant input of domestic sewage, and a possible leaking water main appears to be very reasonable.

REMEDIAL MEASURES

Many bodies remain buried at Mameyes because of the extreme difficulty in excavating the dried landslide material. Therefore, the Puerto Rican government elected to retain a geotechnical consulting firm to recommend measures to stabilize the site and create a memorial park to the victims of the landslide. The marginal stability of the site necessitated a comprehensive regrading and stabilization program. Ponce I & M Engineering Laboratory, Inc. (1986), retained to design the stabilization program, specified the following design parameters.

1. Increase the passive resistance at the toe of the landslide by placing fill compacted to an effective residual friction angle of 36° and a cohesion of 1–14 kPa.

2. Flatten the slope of the hillside to an overall angle of 17.5° by grading benches 3–9 m wide. The maximum allowable slope between benches is 22°.

3. Install surface and subsurface drains to collect storm precipitation and channel it off the landslide area.

Two piezometers and two inclinometers were installed on the landslide to monitor slope movement and changes in ground-water level during construction. Figure 22 shows the site after stabilization.

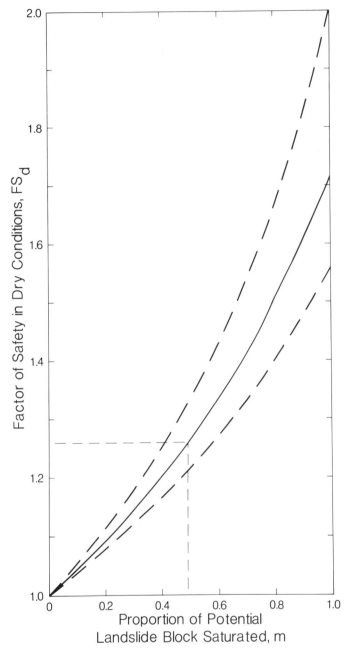

Figure 21. Graph of FS_d, the factor of safety in dry conditions, versus *m*, the proportion of the potential landslide block, measured vertically, that is below the water table. Lines show the failure condition, $FS = 1$, for three material unit weights corresponding to the minimum (19.6 kN/m^3, upper dashed line), maximum (27.5 kN/m^3, lower dashed line), and most probable (23.6 kN/m^3, solid line) unit weights of the material that failed.

Figure 22. Mameyes landslide site after remedial stabilization. Memorial park under construction shown in the foreground. Horizontal features on the slope are terraces with surface drains.

sliding took place in three distinct phases within less than an hour. The first two phases of sliding involved translational sliding of two 12-m-thick slabs of calcareous sandstone bedrock along bedding-plane surfaces parallel to the slope face. The third phase of sliding involved the toppling failure of a block, on the western part of the slide, that disaggregated and formed a rock fall. Subsidiary flow failures onto the toe and from the downstream face of the toe were triggered by the heavy rainfall and the emptying of a water tank, containing as much as 4 million liters of water, onto the slide.

An estimated 120 homes were destroyed by the landslide, and at least 129 people were killed, though only 39 bodies were recovered. This death toll is the largest from a single landslide in North American history.

Calculations of prelandslide slope stability indicate that when the water table was below the potential shear surface, the most likely factor of safety against failure was 1.26. A water table about 6 m above the shear surface, which would saturate half the thickness of the slide block, reduces the factor of safety to 1.0. A water table at this level is a reasonable result of the conditions preceding failure.

The landslide area has been stabilized and was developed as a memorial park to the landslide victims.

ACKNOWLEDGMENTS

Darrell G. Herd and Russell H. Campbell, both of the U.S. Geological Survey, responded initially to the landslide disaster and provided valuable data, including reports of eyewitness accounts. William Cotton, of William Cotton and Associates, accompanied me on part of the field investigation; his observations and insights were very helpful. Ponce I & M Engineering Laboratory generously shared their drilling and laboratory data. David Keefer and Stephen Obermeier reviewed the manuscript and provided helpful comments on its improvement.

SUMMARY

The landslide that destroyed the neighborhood at Mameyes was triggered by a major tropical storm that probably produced more than 450 mm of rainfall at the site in 24 hr. The major

REFERENCES CITED

Campbell, R. H., 1975, Soil slips, debris flows, and rainstorms in the Santa Monica Mountains and vicinity, southern California: U.S. Geological Survey Professional Paper 851, 51 p.

Campbell, R. H., Herd, D. G., and Alonso, R. M., 1985, Preliminary response activities and recommendations of the USGS landslide hazard research team to the Puerto Rico landslide disaster of October 7, 1985: U.S. Geological Survey Open-File Report 85-719, 13 p.

Campbell, R. H., Herd, D. G., and Jibson, R. W., 1986, Preliminary review of the landslide disaster of October 7, 1985, near Ponce, Puerto Rico: Geological Society of America Abstracts with Programs, v. 18, p. 92–93.

Federal Emergency Management Agency, 1985, Interagency hazard mitigation report FEMA-746-DR-PR: New York, Federal Emergency Management Agency Region II, Federal Interagency Flood Hazard Mitigation Team Report for Puerto Rico, 65 p.

Jibson, R. W., 1986, Evaluation of landslide hazards resulting from the 5–8 October 1985, storm in Puerto Rico: U.S. Geological Survey Open-File Report 86-26, 40 p.

Krushensky, R. D., and Monroe, W. H., 1975, Geologic map of the Ponce quadrangle, Puerto Rico: U.S. Geological Survey Miscellaneous Investigations Map I-863, scale 1:20,000.

Lambe, T. W., and Whitman, R. V., 1969, Soil mechanics: New York, John Wiley and Sons, 553 p.

Maury, C. J., 1929, Porto Rican and Dominican stratigraphy: Science, new ser., v. 70, p. 609.

Monroe, W. H., 1973, Stratigraphy and petroleum possibilities of middle Tertiary rocks in Puerto Rico: American Association of Petroleum Geologists Bulletin, v. 57, no. 6, p. 1086–1099.

Monroe, W. H., 1980, Some tropical landforms of Puerto Rico: U.S. Geological Survey Professional Paper 1159, 39 p.

National Oceanic and Atmospheric Administration, 1985, Climatological data, Puerto Rico and the Virgin Islands, 1985: v. 31, nos. 1–12.

Ponce I & M Engineering Laboratory, Inc., 1986, Geotechnical report for the soil stabilization at Mameyes landslide area, Portugues Urbano Ward, Ponce, Puerto Rico (Report prepared for the Puerto Rico National Guard and the Commonwealth of Puerto Rico): Ponce, Puerto Rico, Ponce I & M Engineering Laboratory, Inc., 76 p.

U.S. Geological Survey, 1985, Water resources in Puerto Rico and the Virgin Islands—A review: U.S. Geological Survey, Caribbean District of the Water Resources Division, v. 4, no. 7, 7 p.

Manuscript Accepted by the Society February 21, 1992

Geological Society of America
Reviews in Engineering Geology, Volume IX
1992

Chapter 6

Landslide failure at 20510 Callon Drive, Topanga, California, March 1978

Arthur G. Keene*
County Geologist (Retired), Los Angeles County, Department of Public Works, Los Angeles, California 90020

ABSTRACT

During the months between December 1, 1977, and March 31, 1978, 51.7 (~131 cm) of rain fell in the area of Topanga Canyon, California. This winter rain appears to have been the underlying cause of many landslides, slump debris flows, and mudflows. One such failure occurred at 20510 Callon Drive, Topanga. This site consisted of a 3:1 northwest-facing slope covered by 4 to 20 ft (~1.2–60 m) of colluvium and soil over Topanga sandstone, shale, and basalt—apparently in place, as indicated by a local consulting firm. The area containing the site was mapped by the U.S. Geological Survey as a landslide. The landslide's validity was discounted by the consultant geologist on the basis of his field investigation and five exploratory trenches. Lacking evidence of an existing landslide, the consultant recommended that slabs on grade be designed for expansive soil conditions, and footing be extended through the creep-prone soil to derive support in bedrock. The consultant observed that, prior to sliding, the site was affected by minor slumping in the road cut along Callon Drive.

By December 1977, the owner noticed the effects of instability. Movement worsened to the point of general failure at a rate of 2 to 4 in (~5–10 cm) per day. The site was essentially destroyed due to landslide movement, and by a mysterious fire, by March 27, 1978. Application for a building permit was made on January 16, 1976. Orders to demolish were given by June 2, 1978; this constitutes a very short period of service for the structure.

Ground failure consisted of a block rotational slide, ~200 ft in length by 100 ft wide (~60 × 30 m). Its thickness is 10 to 20 ft (~3–6 m) with a 6-ft-high (~1.8 m) scarp inclined about 60°. The foot terminates on the south side of Callon Drive and above the road surface.

Two 25-ft-deep (~6 m) seepage pits were emplaced near the roadside, a location not recommended by the consultant. Instability resulted from saturation of creep-prone colluvium and soil mantle and underlying fragmental Conejo volcanic breccia, which is mixed locally with sandstone and siltstone blocks and debris from the Cold Creek Member of the Topanga Group Formation.

Three separate lawsuits ensued against the consultant, the builder, and the County of Los Angeles. Ultimate damage awarded to the owner amounted to $135,000.

INTRODUCTION

As a single example of physical damage and monetary damage in ground failures in the urban setting, the landslide failure at 20510 Callon Drive, Topanga, California, during March 1978

seems to lend itself well as a minor but typical example of a landslide failure and its effect on the individual in today's complicated, litigious society in the State of California.

Southern California underwent one of its worst cyclic wet periods in the winter of 1977–1978, having received 51.7 in

---

*Present address: 2601 East Victoria Street, #308, Rancho Dominguez, California 90220.

Keene, A. G., 1992, Landslide failure at 20510 Callon Drive, Topanga, California, March 1978, *in* Slosson, J. E., Keene, A. G., and Johnson, J. A., eds., Landslides/Landslide Mitigation: Boulder, Colorado, Geological Society of America Reviews in Engineering Geology, v. IX.

(~131 cm) of rain in the Santa Monica Mountains; almost 18 in (~46 cm) fell on Callon Drive in March. Prior to these rains, the site was vacant land, having little forestation, a hummocky appearance, an intermittent small spring, and a grassy gentle slope having a less-than 3:1 gradient.

A speculative structure was built during 1976–1977 under the aegis of the Los Angeles County Building Code and its explicit geologic hazard prevention laws and regulations. The house was sold to Mr. and Mrs. Richard August in September 1977, and was completely destroyed by 1978 by an earthflow slide followed by a fire.

Other than the incident rainfall, local seepage from the site's sewage disposal system and neighboring seepage pits, coupled with inherent spring activity resulting from migrating percolating rainwater from higher ground sources, undoubtedly led to loss of strength in the colluvial mass topographically above Callon Drive.

Topographic relief from the high near the south boundary to the low at the northeast corner of the lot is about 30 ft (~9 m).

Law suits were initiated by the Augusts against the County of Los Angeles, the consultant engineering geologist, and the builder, and the First Federal Savings and Loan Association of Santa Monica instituted a suit against the builder. The Red Carpet Realty was also sued. The Augusts were eventually awarded $135,000 in 1982, to be shared equally with the First Federal Savings and Loan Association in satisfaction of the outstanding loan.

BASIC GEOLOGY OF THE SITE AND MECHANICS OF LANDSLIDING

Regional geology

The geologic map by Yerkes and Campbell (1980) shows that the site of the landslide is underlain at depth by the Topanga Formation, consisting of marine sandstone, siltstone, and pebbly sandstone of the Cold Creek Member, which is in turn overlain by volcanic breccia of the Conejo Volcanics, which contain some thin limestone beds. The downslope edge is along Garapito Creek. The slide terrain as mapped by the U.S. Geological Survey appears to be controlled by erosional undercutting of northward-dipping beds. The slide's head scarp is basically in the vicinity of 20526 Callon Drive (Fig. 1).

Mechanics of slide

The landslide, about 200 ft long and 100 ft wide (~60 × 30 m), was basically an earthflow incorporating the weathered remnants and fragmental blocks of the Conejo Volcanics and Topanga Formation sandstones and shales in a matrix of a deep colluvial mass. Though distress was noted in December 1977, this mass was mobilized by (1) a heavy rainfall in 1978, probably influenced by on-site sewage disposal improperly placed north of the residence and above the north-facing slope of Callon Drive

and (2) by intermittent spring activity. These relations are presented in Figure 1.

Underlying unstable bedrock conditions may be represented by shallow daylighted components of the dips, thus providing the potential instability along strike components of the bedded materials. Observations by the consultant firm, representing the developer, led to the probably erroneous conclusion that bedrock materials were intensely folded but in place, and covered by a thin soil mantle subject to downslope gravitational creep.

Exploratory work accomplished prior to construction at 20510 Callon Drive

The controlling agency, the Building and Safety Division of the former Department of the County Engineer, represented by the Engineering Geology Section of the Design Division advising the Building and Safety Division, indicated to the developer that the proposed site for development was located in the head scarp area of a landslide mapped by the U.S. Geological Survey (Yerkes and others, 1973). Consequently, a geologic investigation was required prior to the issuance of a permit for construction.

Subsequent exploration of the site by the consultant firm (Merrill, 1974), using five relatively shallow trenches (Fig. 2), concluded that siltstones, clays, and sandstones were dipping steeply north and moderately steeply to the south, and therefore represented, in the opinion of the consultant, sediments intruded by a basalt along a fault contact (as exposed in the southernmost trench). The consultant further concluded that the basalt could be correlated with in-place basalt farther to the south and west of the site. On page 5 of his report, the consultant states: "Although the U.S. Geological Survey (1973) identified the site and environs as part of a large ancient landslide, exploration disproved this conclusively. Rather, the site is underlain by moderately deformed sediments and none of the bedrock is part of a landslide. The character of outcrops and trench exposures is such that the rocks are clearly in-place." The consultant did note that the "adobe soil mantle" was creep prone, and that local slumping of the south slope of Callon Drive was evident. No mention of a spring in the adjacent drainage east of the lot was made in the report.

Analysis of data by the consultant, using his previous experience in the area, field mapping of outcrops, the five trench logs, and a north-south geologic cross-section limited to the length of the lot, showed him that bedrock materials were in place, but in my opinion, bedrock materials were projected much deeper than could be reasonably interpreted by the shallow trenches. The maximum depth of the so-called "soil profile" was in trench 5, in which expansive, creep-prone, dark brown, sandy clay was exposed in the slope adjacent to Callon Drive. Trench 3, upslope and in proximity to the consultant's mapped contact with basalt, exposed 4 ft (~1.2 m) of soil profile described as "stiff fissured dark brown sandy clay." In no case was a trench excavated deeper than 8 ft (~2.4 m). The deepest trench exposed 6.5 ft (~2 m) of sandstone in contact with basalt. However, the exposed head-scarp materials of the landslide, 6 ft high (~1.8 m) and

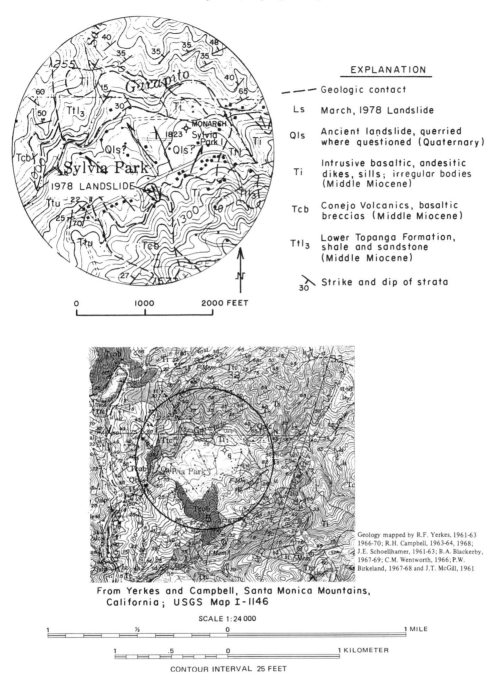

EXPLANATION

- - - Geologic contact

Ls   March, 1978 Landslide

Qls   Ancient landslide, querried where questioned (Quaternary)

Ti   Intrusive basaltic, andesitic dikes, sills; irregular bodies (Middle Miocene)

Tcb   Conejo Volcanics, basaltic breccias (Middle Miocene)

Ttl₃ Lower Topanga Formation, shale and sandstone (Middle Miocene)

30⌐   Strike and dip of strata

0   1000   2000 FEET

Geology mapped by R.F. Yerkes, 1961-63
1966-70; R.H. Campbell, 1963-64, 1968;
J.E. Schoellhamer, 1961-63; B.A. Blackerby,
1967-69; C.M. Wentworth, 1966; P.W.
Birkeland, 1967-68 and J.T. McGill, 1961

From Yerkes and Campbell, Santa Monica Mountains, California; USGS Map I-1146

SCALE 1:24 000

1   ½   0   1 MILE

1   .5   0   1 KILOMETER

CONTOUR INTERVAL 25 FEET

Figure 1. Geologic map and landslide location (after Yerkes and Campbell, 1980).

inclined at 60°, did not appear to be in-place bedrock. Hindsight indicates that a deeper exploratory effort during the initial exploration of the site was needed, and field evidence after slide activation verified this need. The erratic exposures of the soil profile, revealed by the consultant's exploration, further indicates this need and should have been obvious to the consultant. Was a stratified soil profile showing zones of soil development observed? None was reported; only a nondescript variable thickness of adobe was described, which is more typical of an accumulation of colluvium rather than a thin mantle of adobe soil. Deeper exploration, using continuous north-south trenching in combination with at least three borings of nominal depth, could have been initiated to show the absence or the possibility of a slide plane at depth; it may have revealed clearly a colluvial and bedrock continuity representative of truly in-place bedrock, as posed by the consultant (Fig. 3).

Furthermore, in view of the essentially homoclinal structure exposed in adjoining areas outside of the suspected landslides, the

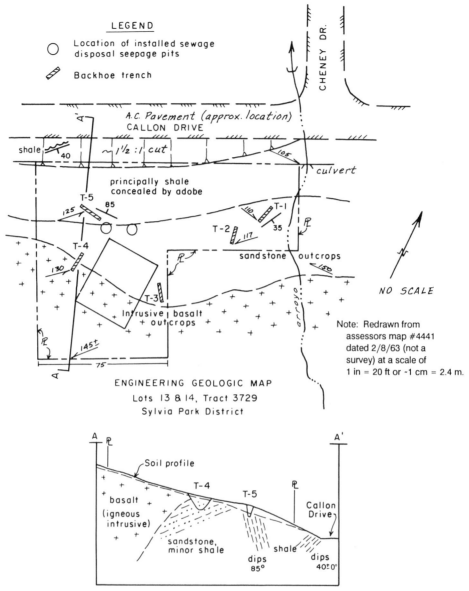

Figure 2. Site geologic map.

consultant should have at least suspected that the irregular structures in his trenches and irregular distribution of lithologies within the short space of the subject lot was possibly caused by disruption of bedrock along strike during landsliding as mapped by the U.S. Geological Survey. Had the county been adequately staffed to inspect the exploration carried out by the consultant, more detailed exploration may have been required. Instead, the county was dependent upon the report and observations of a state registered and certified engineering geologist.

Exploratory work after destruction

No exploratory work has been undertaken since the slide occurred in March 1978, other than nominal field mapping of the landslide's boundaries. To this day, in all fairness to the consultant, the true nature and mechanics of failure have not been precisely determined. However, it is quite certain that the landslide as mapped by the U.S. Geological Survey, based on hummocky terrain and prevailing bedrock structural relations in the contiguous nearby area, was a previously existing landslide activated by intense incident rainfall in 1978.

The depth of the 1978 slide was probably no greater than 10–20 ft (~3–6 m). The position of the toe at Callon Drive is indicated by earthflow and seepage onto the road itself (Figs. 4 and 5). Although a deeper landslide, as mapped by the U.S. Geological Survey, may indeed toe out in Garapito Creek, a shallower portion of the slide was reactivated following saturation as a result of rainfall and perhaps inappropriate location of seepage pits for sewage disposal. Neighboring seepage pits upgradient from the site, and a possible high natural ground-water

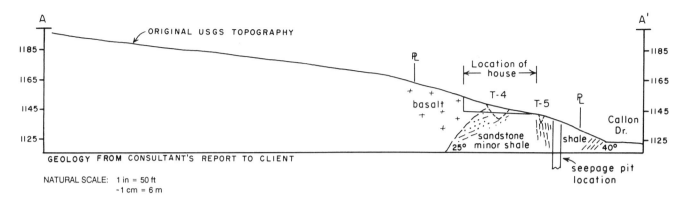

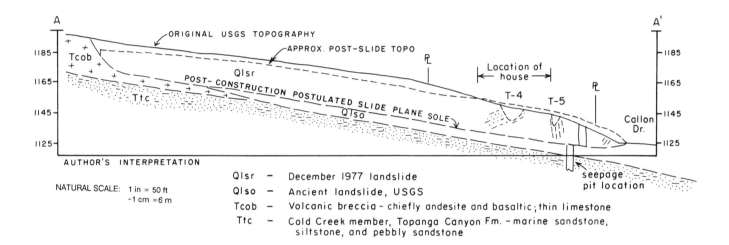

Qlsr — December 1977 landslide
Qlso — Ancient landslide, USGS
Tcob — Volcanic breccia - chiefly andesite and basaltic; thin limestone
Ttc   — Cold Creek member, Topanga Canyon Fm. - marine sandstone,
           siltstone, and pebbly sandstone

(from USGS Map I-1146, Yerks and Campbell, 1980)

Figure 3. Shown above is a geologic profile along section line A-A′ with consultant's interpretation of his exploratory data. Shown below is my interpretation of postslide conditions revealing the relations of a reactivated portion of a previously existing landslide as mapped by the U.S. Geological Survey (Yerkes and Campbell, 1980).

condition, as suggested by the spring, may also have contributed to the saturation. The Los Angeles County Flood Control District recorded 51.7 in (~131 cm) of rain in the area between December 1, 1977, and March 31, 1978, of which 17.6 in (~45 cm) fell in March, as reported by Station #6, Topanga Fire Station, two miles (~3.2 km) away.

Sewage disposal

On page 2 of his report (Merrill, 1974), the consultant clearly suggested that on-site disposal of sewage effluent, "may be effected from a leach field or seepage pits in the southeast portion of the lot." This would be topographically higher than the location of the proposed structure. In the words of Merrill (1974, p. 2), "Waste water should not be discharged near the cut slope along Callon Road where saturation could induce instability." The Geologic Review Sheet from the Engineering Geology Section of the Design Division clearly limited the location of the sewage disposal on site to the "southerly and westernmost portion

of the lot within the basalt," in accordance with the recommendation of the consultant.

Unfortunately, the Department of Health Services Environmental Management approved the location of sewage disposal almost precisely where the consultant and Engineering Geology Section indicated that it should not be placed. The controlling factor in this decision may have been the required drainage gradient from household utilities to the seepage pit. Apparently, the adverse gradient from north to south was not considered to be feasible, resulting in the rejection of the consultant's recommendation. A proper drainage for sewer lines would have required deeper seepage pits and a deep drainage trench from the house to the southern portion of the lot. Though such a design was technically feasible, it would have entailed additional cost.

It is difficult, if not impossible, to ascertain the total effect of improper seepage disposal at this location, but logic clearly indicates that it could not have been placed in a more adverse position to retain inherent stability of the slope above Callon Drive. Incident rainfall probably exacerbated an already-unstable condi-

Figure 4. Oblique aerial photograph showing boundary of landslide at 20510 Callon Drive, taken June, 1, 1978. Note seepage and earthflow features.

tion. However, the seepage pits could not have operated any longer than six months before landsliding occurred.

An alternate seepage design at the location used would have introduced sewage effluent at a depth within bedrock materials below any possible slide plane: this alternative was apparently never considered by the consultant.

Arson

As a sidelight to this unfortunate situation, a mysterious fire broke out in the structure on March 25, 1978, shortly after it had been vacated by the owners. According to reports on file the slide

basically destroyed the house on March 6, 1978: at this time, the slide was moving about 6 in (~15 cm) per day.

The electricity was disconnected and propane tanks removed on March 7, 1978. The Building and Safety Division condemned the house about one week before the fire. The total loss due to fire was estimated at $60,000.

The insurance agent, Burton Duze and Co., agent for the Augusts, stated that the insurance covered fire only and was payable to the First Federal Savings and Loan Association of Santa Monica. The cause of the fire was determined to be from incendiary boosters, started by an open flame located in the living room and second story bedroom and front sundeck. The perpe-

Figure 5. View of 20510 Callon Drive looking toward the south and up slope. Note earthflow features in foreground above Callon Drive. Photograph was taken after March 25 fire, and prior to demolition of structure (August 18, 1978).

trator of the fire was never determined, nor the purpose of the arson.

Damages

A claim against the County of Los Angeles by Mr. and Mrs. Richard August was submitted on June 8, 1978 by Marc Epstein, the August's attorney.

On or about January 26, 1979, the Augusts instituted suit against the county in the Los Angeles Superior Court (Case No. WEC57659), and on November 21, 1978, against the consultant geologist. On November 22, 1978, the First Federal Savings and Loan Association of Santa Monica instituted suit against the builder. All actions were consolidated for all purposes under the Augusts, who, as plaintiffs, collectively sued the builder, the consulting geologist, the real estate company (broker and agent), the architect, and the county.

The claim indicated that damage was apparent on March 8, 1978, and had progressively worsened. The Augusts claimed that the county was "Negligent in the inspection of the building, negligent in issuing permits, failure to advise of dangerous conditions and to properly maintain County property, and was instrumental in increasing the rain which caused the landslide by engaging in cloud seed activity."

The specific allegations against the county were that the county (1) improperly approved the geology reports submitted, thereby allowing the house to be built on a known landslide, (2) allowed on-site sewage seepage pits to be placed in an area where the county geologist had expressly stated they should not

be placed, and (3) violated the order of the Building Rehabilitation Appeals Board regarding the demolition of the structure.

Settlement negotiations held in Department L of the Santa Monica Superior Court resulted in an agreement on June 1, 1982, in which all parties agreed to pay the following amounts totaling $135,000: builder's insurer—$65,000; builder (personally)—$20,000; consulting geologist—$30,000; Red Carpet Realty—$15,000; and the County of Los Angeles—$5,000.

The court-awarded amount of $135,000 was then split between the owner of the destroyed residence and First Federal Savings and Loan Association of Santa Monica.

The plaintiff's property damage alone, ignoring all claims for emotional distress, amounted to $150,000.

Government Code Section 818.4 generally immunizes public entities from liability for license and permit activities, but the California State Supreme Court had held that this immunity is limited to discretionary licensing activities (for example, *Morris versus Marin* (1977) 18, Cal. 3d901). Where a public entity is under mandatory duty, Section 818.4 does not provide immunity.

Section 308(b) of the Los Angeles County Building Code created such mandatory duty: "Work requiring a building or a grading permit by this code is not permitted in an area determined by the County Engineer to be subject to hazard from landslide, settlement, or slippage." The Building and Safety Division (via the Los Angeles County Health Department) did indeed approve and allow placement of sewage seepage pits in an area not authorized by the county geologist. Hence, the county did settle for a negotiated consideration of $5,000 on the strength of the omission by the county. The plaintiffs also alleged that the county's geological review sheet was inadequate, but this allegation appears not to have been considered in the Agreement of Compromise and General Release entered upon the record before Judge Wolf in the Western District of the Los Angeles Superior Court on May 27, 1982.

CONCLUSIONS

That a landslide, actually an earthflow, did occur on or before March 4, 1978, is irrefutable. By concurrence of all parties involved, it is understood that the geologic investigation was inadequate in that the potential for earthflow was not thoroughly investigated and analyzed. In addition, it would appear that the review of the geologic report by the county geologist was not thorough enough, and should have (1) required the consultant to consider an earthflow mode of failure and (2) considered the possible introduction of sewage effluent via seepage pits placed well into firm bedrock materials below any potential landslide plane, as projected by the U.S. Geological Survey geologic mapping in the vicinity of 20510 Callon Drive.

The review by the permit-issuing agency should also have been more insistent on requiring more conclusive data to support the consulting firm's opinion that the geomorphology did not represent a landslide. Also, the Health Department, as the review agency, should have located the seepage pits where they were recommended by the consultant firm, and not in the slope above the road cut along Callon Drive.

As a condition of approval by the Geology Section, the building inspector and permit issuer were supposed to limit construction and seepage pits in the southern, not northern, part of the lot. This was not done.

Had exploration been accomplished off site and upslope (to the south), across the boundary of the slide mapped by the U.S. Geological Survey, the scarp relation of the ancient slide could have led to a much better understanding of the hummocky terrain observed by the U.S. Geological Survey. Instead, exploratory trenches of relatively shallow depth were placed, apparently without any strategy.

Deep continuous trenches and deep boring control are needed to refute otherwise suspicious geomorphic features resembling landslide-prone terrain.

Variable attitudes at shallow depth should not be construed to be representative of structural control; they may well be disoriented blocks of competent bedrock materials incorporated in a matrix of unconsolidated creep-prone colluvium.

Regional geologic structures should be considered in detail. A consultant should not limit analysis to the immediate site of the project. Of notice in this case is the absence of bedrock attitudes taken by the U.S. Geological Survey geologist in the area they mapped as landslide, whereas attitudes on the flanks of the slide and above the area mapped as landslide reflected a fairly consistent northwest-dipping homoclinal structural relation down to Garapito Creek.

REFERENCES CITED

Los Angeles Superior Court, Case No. WEC57659 August, Richard L. et al. versus County of Los Angeles.

Merrill, J. D., 1974, Engineering geologic report, Lot 13, and portion Lot 14, tract 3729 Callon Drive and Cheney Road, Topanga, Ca.: Los Angeles County, California, Department of Public Works, Engineering Geology Group, Land Development Division Project 42580.

Yerkes, R. F., and Campbell, R. H., 1980, Geologic map of the east-central Santa Monica Mountains, Los Angeles County, California: U.S. Geological Survey Miscellaneous Investigations Map I-1146, scale 1:24,000.

Yerkes, R. F., Campbell, R. H., Schoellhamer, J. E., and Birkeland, P. W., 1973, Preliminary geologic map of the unincorporated part of the Topanga quadrangle, Los Angeles County, California: U.S. Geological Survey Open-File Report, scale 1:12,000, 1 sheet.

MANUSCRIPT ACCEPTED BY THE SOCIETY FEBRUARY 21, 1992

Geological Society of America
Reviews in Engineering Geology, Volume IX
1992

Chapter 7

Landslide mitigation using horizontal drains, Pacific Palisades area, Los Angeles, California

James P. Krohn
GeoSoils, Inc., 6634 Valjean Avenue, Van Nuys, California 91406

ABSTRACT

Horizontal drains have been successfully used for a number of years in many areas for improving slope stability within landslide and/or landslide-prone areas. One such application of their use is discussed relative to a more than 66-m-high (220+ ft) 2:1 (26°) southwest-facing cut slope located in the Pacific Palisades area of the city of Los Angeles, California.

The slope is somewhat unusual in that the geologic structure of the bedrock (i.e., siltstone) appears to be neutral and/or favorable relative to the orientation of the slope surface. However, the slope underwent minor downslope movement (i.e., sagging, creep) following the heavy rains of 1978. Manifested mostly by cracks within paved terrace drains and/or downdrains, the movement appears to be related to local perched ground water and a northwest-southeast–trending fault zone that cuts across the southern part of the slope.

Horizontal drains are currently being used to improve slope stability by reducing the amount of ground water, especially within the vicinity of the fault zone. Ground water was encountered in 11 of the 16 horizontal drains; initial flow rates were up to 5.7 l (1.5 gal) per minute. Calculations suggest that the dewatering of the slope could increase slope stability to a factor of safety of more than 1.5.

INTRODUCTION

Horizontal drains have been successfully used for improving slope stability within landslide-prone areas. Once such application of their use is currently being attempted on a 66-m-high (220 ft) 2:1 (26°) cut slope located within the Pacific Palisades area of the city of Los Angeles, California. The purpose of the drains is to reduce excessive hydrostatic pressure that may have built up behind the slope; this hydrostatic pressure is believed to represent a major contributing factor to the recent movement of the slope.

PROJECT HISTORY

Prior to tract development, the slope represented part of a large northeast-southwest–trending ridgeline, bordered on either side by similarly trending canyons. However, as residential development began in this area in the middle 1970s, it became necessary to grade the ridgeline to create additional buildable areas, as

well as to generate fill material needed for nearby canyons. Grading of the slope began in late 1973 and continued through early 1974. This grading involved removal of bedrock up to 30 m (100 ft) below the original ground surface.

The slope is ~66 m (220 ft) in maximum vertical height and has an approximate gradient of 2:1 or flatter. It is multisided, consisting of three slope faces oriented approximately at right angles to one another. The largest of the slope faces is southwest facing, located farthest to the north, and is underlain by bedrock. The two smaller slope faces are northwest and southwest facing, and represent the middle and southernmost parts of the slope, respectively. Both of these slopes represent stabilization fills. The ridge area directly above these two stabilization fills is now at a gradient that is generally flatter than 3:1 (18°) (see Figs. 1 and 2).

Initially, the three slope faces were designed so that the northern and southern parts of the slope would be west facing and the middle slope north facing. However, this slope configura-

Krohn, J. P., 1992, Landslide mitigation using horizontal drains, Pacific Palisades area, Los Angeles, California, *in* Slosson, J. E., Keene, A. G., and Johnson, J. A., eds., Landslides/Landslide Mitigation: Boulder, Colorado, Geological Society of America Reviews in Engineering Geology, v. IX.

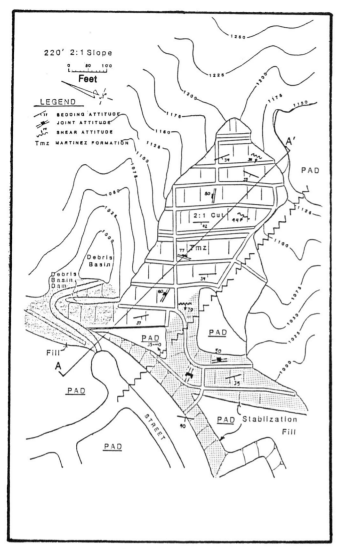

Figure 1. Geologic map.

Figure 2. Present configuration of slope.

tion was modified prior to grading in order to conform with the local geologic conditions. This modification essentially involved reorienting the three slope faces to a northwest and/or southwest direction, so that each of the slope faces would be either parallel to or perpendicular to the strike of the bedding.

GEOLOGIC CONDITIONS

Where bedrock is exposed in the slope, it consists chiefly of siltstone of the Paleocene Martinez Formation. At the time of grading, the siltstone varied from highly weathered to unweathered. However, subsequent to grading the slope has been subject to air slaking and, therefore, most of the outer portion of the slope now appears to be weathered. The siltstone ranges from massive to crudely, indistinctly bedded, and is locally highly concretion-

ary. Bedding within the slope appears to trend northwest to northeast; west to southwest dips range predominantly from 30° to 50°: the bedding is generally steeper than the gradient of the slope.

Most of the siltstone appears to be highly fractured and jointed. There are at least two principal joint and/or shear trends, and numerous smaller secondary joints and shears. The principal joints and/or shears have strikes of east-west and northeast-southwest. Although they vary locally in dip direction, most of the joints and/or shears dip steeply (50° to vertical). The joints and/or shears are for the most part steeper than the slope gradient.

During grading, a northwest-southeast–trending fault zone was observed between the larger southwest-facing slope and the smaller northwest-facing slope (see Fig. 1). Bedrock within the fault zone appeared to be highly fractured and contained numerous shear surfaces (i.e., adverse shears relative to the northwest-facing slope). Although numerous shears were noted within the fault zone, the most prominent shears had northeasterly dips of 35° to 40°. Most of the fault zone is no longer visible; it is covered

Figure 3. Failure in slope during grading in 1974.

by the stabilization fill that was placed against the northwest-facing slope (see Fig. 1).

SLOPE FAILURE

A failure occurred within the northwest-facing part of the slope during grading in early 1974 (see Fig. 3). This failure occurred along the previously mentioned fault zone following a period of heavy rainfall. Correction of the failure included removal of the slide debris and the construction of a 12–18-m-wide (40–60 ft) stabilization fill along the northwest-facing slope and along the southwest-facing slope located farther to the south. In addition, the area above these two stabilization fills was laid back to a gradient flatter than 3:1 (see Figs. 1 and 2). Only this area, as well as the large southwest-facing slope to the north, remained as a cut area.

Following the completion of grading, the slope performed satisfactorily for approximately four years until the heavy rains of 1977–1978. In March 1978, numerous cracks were observed on and close to the slope. The cracks were observed in the bedrock and paved slope terrace drains and/or downdrains, as well as in the adjoining area to the northwest (i.e., the desilting basin dam and nearby street cul-de-sac). Vertical movement within the paved terrace drains and/or downdrains ranged from 0.63 to 30.5 cm (0.25 to 12 in) (average 1.26 to 5 cm), and horizontal movement ranged from 0.63 to 20.3 cm (0.25 to 8 in) (average 1.26 to 2.54 cm). The most severe cracking was observed along the fault zone. Field work after slope movement included (1) mapping of existing cracks, (2) establishing a survey network of 13 points (11 of which remain functional), (3) excavation of

four borings (two of which were converted to dewatering wells), and (4) installation of horizontal drains.

HORIZONTAL DRAINS

Water seepage is apparent along the south side of the large cut slope (i.e., along the fault zone), as well as at the toe of the northwest-facing stabilization fill and in the nearby street. Thus, there appears to be little doubt that water (i.e., locally perched ground water) has been a major contributing factor to the observed slope movement.

A total of 16 horizontal drains were installed using a rotary wash drill rig which, in turn, drilled a 7.62 to 10.16 cm (3 to 4 in) diameter hole. Twelve of the drains were installed in March 1985; the remaining four drains were installed approximately one year later. (Note that, although backdrains were placed behind the northwest-facing stabilization fill, it is suspected that a portion of the backdrain system may be malfunctioning. Therefore, the last four horizontal drains were installed through the stabilization fill in an attempt to further improve drainage in this area.) At the completion of drilling, 1.5–2.5-in-diameter (3.8–6.35 cm) slotted PVC pipe was inserted into the holes to ensure that there would be a continuous opening from the back of each of the holes to the face of the slope. Lengths of the horizontal drains ranged from 81 to 258 m (270 to 860 ft) and were drilled into the slope at locations shown in Fig. 4. A positive flow gradient of at least 5% was recommended for each of the drains. Initially, the largest flow of 5.7 l (1.5 gal) per minute was obtained from horizontal drain III-3. However, five of the drains produced no water at all following installation, and only half of the drains currently yield water (see Table 1). Most of the water being drained appears to represent local pockets of perched water trapped along joints, shears, and/or bedding in proximity to the fault zone.

RESULTS AND DISCUSSION

On the basis of available data, the failure of the slope appears to be in a west to northwest direction (see Fig. 5). Surface cracks both on and in proximity to the slope suggest relatively deep-seated movement, probably 15 to 30 m (50 to 100 ft) beneath the slope surface. The data further suggest that movement may be the product of randomly oriented shears, joints, and bedding-plane surfaces that have apparently coalesced together to form a series of subparallel slip planes. These coalescing slip surfaces, together with the fault zone along the south side of the large cut slope, appear to represent the controlling factor of the slope movement (see Fig. 6). The bedrock is therefore subject to creep, sagging, and possible consolidation under saturated conditions or when seepage forces are applied (i.e., from local pockets of perched ground water).

Surface surveys began on April 3, 1978; four surveys were taken during April and May 1978. Another set of readings was taken in May and November 1980. A seventh set of readings was taken in February 1985, and the most recent set of readings was taken in January 1986. Review of the data indicates that the slope has moved vertically more than 5 cm (2 in) between 1978 and 1986, ~12.7 cm (5 in) of horizontal movement occurring in a west-northwest direction. The upper part of the slope appears to be dropping, whereas the lower part is moving up. The greatest amount of upward movement (i.e., 5 cm) is located in proximity to Settlement Monument 7. There has been no horizontal movement and only minor settlement (less than 1.27 cm [0.5 in]) within the past year, since the horizontal drains were installed in March 1985. The movement that was observed occurred at the

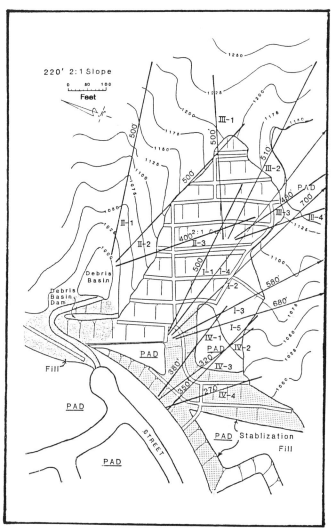

Figure 4. Horizon drain location map.

TABLE 1. HORIZONTAL DRAIN FLOW RATES

Drain Number	Inspection Dates							
	4/8/85	4/17/85	12/26/85	2/17/86	3/27/86	5/27/86	6/26/86	8/8/86
	Flow Rates–Gallons per Minute							
I-1	Dry	Dry	0.5	0.5	Dry	Dry	Dry	Dry
I-2	1.7	1.6	0.5	0.7	1.0	Drip	0.1	Drip
I-3	1.2	0.8	0.5	0.5	0.5	0.3	0.2	0.2
I-4	Dry	Dry	Drip	0.5	0.6	0.6	0.5	0.5
I-5		Dry	Drip	Drip	Drip	Drip	Drip	Drip
II-1		Dry	0.5	0.4	Dry	Drip	0.2	Drip
II-2		Dry	Dry	Dry	Dry	Dry	Dry	Dry
II-3		Dry	Dry	Dry	Dry	Dry	Dry	Dry
III-1		Dry	Dry	Dry	Drip	Dry	Dry	Dry
III-2		0.6	Dry	Dry	Drip	Dry	Dry	Dry
III-3		1.5	1.2	2.0	1.5	1.5	2.0	1.7
III-4		Dry	Dry	Dry	Dry	Dry	Dry	Dry
IV-1						0.4	Drip	Drip
IV-2							0.3	0.3
IV-3							0.25	0.25
IV-4						Drip	0.25	0.1

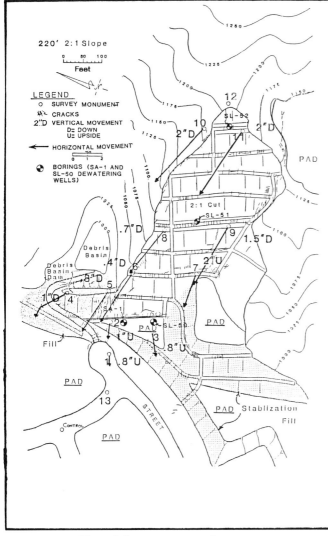

Figure 5. Survey monument data map.

top of the debris basin located immediately north of the cut slope (see Fig. 5).

Stability analysis of the slope generally indicated that the factor of safety prior to installation of the horizontal drains was between 1 and 1.5. Judging from the quality and source of flow issuing from the horizontal drains, and where water was encountered during drilling of the horizontal drains, it appears that the fault zone along the south side of the large cut slope acts as a ground-water barrier. Penetration of this fault by some of the drains has apparently had the effect of drawing some of the ground water away from this critical area. Additional stability analyses indicate that reduction of the locally perched water conditions by the installation of the horizontal drains and pumping of the two dewatering wells (i.e., SA-1 and SL-50) could conceivably increase the calculated factor of safety for the slope to greater than 1.5.

SUMMARY

1. A slope failure occurred in a 66-m-high (220 ft), 2:1 cut slope underlain by what would normally be considered favorable or neutral geologic conditions. That is, the strike of the bedding, joints, and shears trend either parallel or perpendicular to the slope, and respective dips are equal to or steeper than the slope gradient.

2. The bedrock within the slope is subject to creep, sagging, and possible consolidation under saturated conditions or when seepage forces are applied (i.e., from local pockets of perched ground water).

3. Movement of the slope appears to be controlled by several slip surfaces (i.e., bedding, joints, shears) together with a fault zone that is located along the southern end of the cut slope.

4. Installation of horizontal drains has apparently improved the stability of the subject slope. Although it would be premature

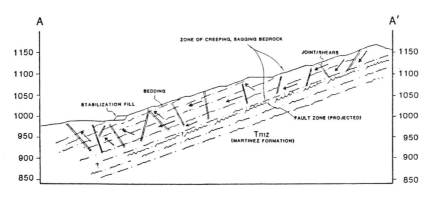

Note: Horizontal Scale (Feet) = Vertical Scale (Feet)

Figure 6. Geologic cross-section A-A'.

to say that a factor of safety of 1.5 has been reached at this time, in that some movement (1.27 cm [0.5 in]) has apparently occurred within the past year (1986). However, stability calculations indicate that a factor of safety of greater than 1.5 is possible, providing that the horizontal drains remain functional, the paved terrace drains and/or downdrains are maintained, and the two dewatering wells at the toe of slope are pumped on a regular basis.

MANUSCRIPT ACCEPTED BY THE SOCIETY FEBRUARY 21, 1992

Geological Society of America
Reviews in Engineering Geology, Volume IX
1992

Chapter 8

Ground water in the Abalone Cove landslide, Palos Verdes Peninsula, southern California

Kathleen A. Proffer
WZI Inc., 4800 Easton Drive, Suite 114, Bakersfield, California 93309

ABSTRACT

The Abalone Cove landslide, in southern California, is an 80 acre (32 ha) landslide within an ~870 acre (348 ha) ancient landslide complex. The landslide has developed in seaward-dipping marine strata of the middle Miocene Monterey Formation. The lower part of the landslide began moving by February 1974; the upper part did not appear to start moving until the spring of 1978. Since 1980, landslide movement has been controlled by the removal of ground water from the landslide mass.

During years of nearly normal rainfall, subsurface inflow was the major source of ground water, contributing 55%. Percolation of rainfall and of delivered water were second and third, contributing 22% and 19%, respectively. During years of nearly twice normal rainfall, percolation of rainfall was the major source of ground water, contributing 56%. Subsurface inflow, percolation of delivered water, and surface inflow contributed 27%, 9%, and 8%, respectively.

Prior to the installation of seven dewatering wells, the major loss of ground water was discharge to the surface by seeps at the toe of the landslide. The seeps accounted for 81% of the ground-water disposal. During the last two years of the study when the dewatering system was fully operational, surface seeps accounted for 34% of the ground-water disposal and pumping accounted for 54%. Other sources of ground-water disposal were evapotranspiration and subsurface outflow.

INTRODUCTION

The Abalone Cove landslide is on the south flank of the Palos Verdes Peninsula in southern California, a northwest-trending dome-shaped ridge about 9 mi (14.4 km) long by 5 mi (8 km) wide that bounds the southwest margin of the Los Angeles Coastal Plain (Fig. 1). The peninsula is bordered by the Pacific Ocean on the south and west, the Los Angeles and Long Beach harbors on the east, and the coastal plain of Los Angeles County on the north. The crest of the peninsula rises to an altitude of 1,480 ft (444 m) at San Pedro Hill.

The Abalone Cove landslide occupies the southwestern 80 acres (32 ha) of an 870 acre (348 ha) ancient landslide complex (Fig. 2). The active Portuguese Bend landslide is a 270 acre (108 ha) landslide located just east of the Abalone Cove landslide within the same ancient landslide complex. The Portuguese Bend landslide began moving in 1956. Landsliding within the ancient landslide complex has occurred sporadically for the past 500,000(?) years (Lass and Eagen, 1982).

The Abalone Cove landslide does not appear to have undergone any historic movement prior to its activation in 1974. Landslide movement began within the Abalone Cove part of the Los Angeles County Beach property, seaward of Palos Verdes Drive South (Fig. 3) by February 1974 (Larue, 1976), and probably continued intermittently until the spring of 1978, when it accelerated and activated a landslide mass north of Palos Verdes Drive South. Movement in the area north of Palos Verdes Drive South appears to have begun during the spring of 1978. However, the development of surface ruptures and significant displacement along surface ruptures (on the order of inches and fractions of an inch) in the area along Palos Verdes Drive South appear to have occurred sometime between August 1978, when I first observed these features, and November 4, 1978, when I began monitoring landslide movement.

Proffer, K. A., 1992, Ground water in the Abalone Cove landslide, Palos Verdes Peninsula, southern California, *in* Slosson, J. E., Keene, A. G., and Johnson, J. A., eds., Landslides/Landslide Mitigation: Boulder, Colorado, Geological Society of America Reviews in Engineering Geology, v. IX.

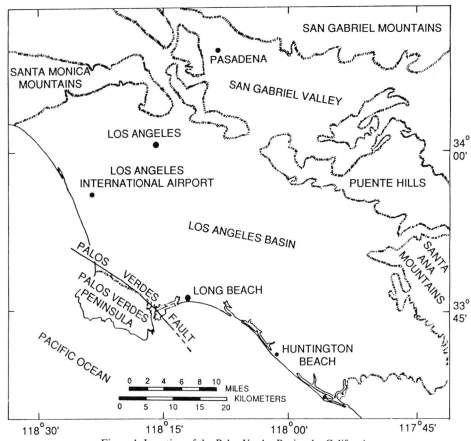

Figure 1. Location of the Palos Verdes Peninsula, California.

A preliminary investigation of the Abalone Cove landslide was completed in February 1979 (Robert Stone & Associates, Inc., 1979a). Ground water was concluded to be the short-term agent responsible for the landslide reactivation. Wave erosion and an inherently weak seaward-dipping bentonite layer at the base of the ancient landslide are the long-term causes of instability. A subsequent investigation determined that dewatering of the landslide would be feasible, provided a minimum of six vertical wells were used (Robert Stone & Associates, Inc., 1979b). In 1979 and 1980, the homeowners in the Abalone Cove area funded the installation of the six-well dewatering system, and the installation of two additional dewatering wells. At present the dewatering system is maintained and improved by the Abalone Cove Landslide Abatement District.

The time period chosen for the ground-water study (Ehlig, 1986) was from hydrologic year 1976–1977 (from October 1, 1976, to September 30, 1977) through hydrologic year 1981–1982. The study period included both wet and dry years. The period was preceded by a series of years of essentially normal to less than normal rainfall (Fig. 4). The study period ended with two dry years, 1980–1981 and 1981–1982. The wet years were abnormally wet; rainfall during hydrologic year 1977–1978 was

approximately twice the normal amount. The study period chosen cannot be considered a standard base hydrologic period because the cumulative departure from the mean rainfall at the beginning and at the end of the study are not the same.

Approximately half of the Abalone Cove landslide is within the Altamira drainage basin. The Altamira drainage basin drains an area of ~820 acres (328 ha), and includes several housing tracts near the crest of the ridge (Fig. 5). The remainder of the Abalone Cove landslide is either drained locally into the ocean or into closed depressions within the landslide. Approximately 28% of the Abalone Cove landslide is developed and 35% of the Altamira drainage basin is developed.

The Abalone Cove landslide is within a ground-water basin that includes the ancient landslide complex (Figs. 2 and 5). Boundaries of the ground-water basin are essentially the same as those of the ancient landslide complex.

GEOLOGY

Geologic units and their water-bearing characteristics

The Abalone Cove landslide has developed within the Altamira Shale Member of the Monterey Formation, more specifi-

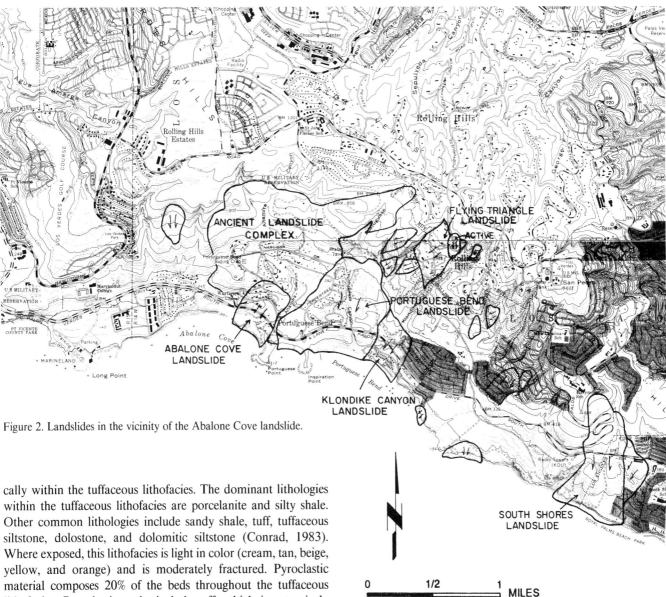

Figure 2. Landslides in the vicinity of the Abalone Cove landslide.

cally within the tuffaceous lithofacies. The dominant lithologies within the tuffaceous lithofacies are porcelanite and silty shale. Other common lithologies include sandy shale, tuff, tuffaceous siltstone, dolostone, and dolomitic siltstone (Conrad, 1983). Where exposed, this lithofacies is light in color (cream, tan, beige, yellow, and orange) and is moderately fractured. Pyroclastic material composes 20% of the beds throughout the tuffaceous lithofacies. Pyroclastic rocks include tuff, which is extensively altered to bentonite, tuffaceous sandstone, siltstone, and mudstone. Tuff beds less than 3 ft (0.9 m) thick are common throughout the lithofacies. A prominent tuff unit, the Portuguese Tuff, is present at the base of the Abalone Cove landslide and the ancient landslide complex. It is typically 40 to 60 ft (1.2–1.8 m) thick and is a composite unit consisting of numerous tuff beds. The entire sequence is bentonitic as a result of diagenic alteration of glass to smectite (primarily sodium montmorillonite; Novak, 1982). Much of the landsliding in the Abalone Cove area has occurred at or near the base of the Portuguese Tuff. The tuff is exposed in the surf zone, at the toe of the landslide, and on the west side of Abalone Cove, west of the landslide.

Basalt, generally in the form of sills, is present within the tuffaceous lithofacies. The basalt is part of an extensive shallow intrusion exposed just east of the ancient landslide complex. Within the Abalone Cove area, basalt is exposed in Altamira

Canyon just south of Palos Verdes Drive South (Fig. 3) and in the lower part of Portuguese Point. The bottom of dewatering well number one (WW-1) is in basalt.

The in-place tuffaceous lithofacies has a low permeability due to the fine-grained nature of the dominant and common rock types. The in-place bedrock is moderately fractured; however, clay from bentonitic tuff commonly seals or fills in these fractures, resulting in a low permeability for the unit. Tuff layers up to 3 ft (0.9 m) thick serve as aquitards that impede vertical groundwater flow within the tuffaceous lithofacies. The Portuguese Tuff serves as an aquiclude. The basalt, if fractured, can serve as a very good aquifer.

The ancient landslide complex consists of large-scale glide

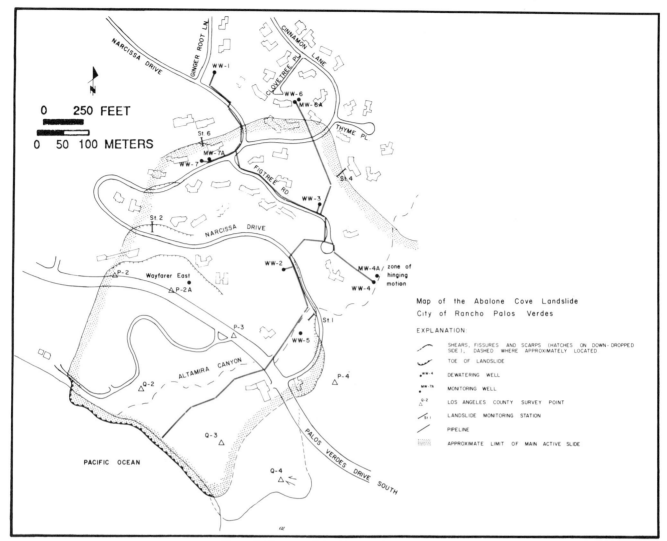

Figure 3. Site map of the Abalone Cove landslide.

blocks and smaller rotational and slump-type failures. The material within the glide blocks has the characteristics and appearance of in-place bedrock. However, graben and scarp areas consist of highly fractured bedrock material in a clay matrix. The clay matrix is largely the result of washing in of clay since sliding occurred: because of this, the permeability (hydraulic conductivity) has declined through time. Permeability is greater in the old alluvial gravels that backfill channels cut in the ancient slide debris. Such channels, which are younger than at least some of the ancient sliding, tend to have better north to south permeability than the ancient slide mass, which is highly compartmented.

Within the Abalone Cove landslide mass, fracturing has caused a great increase in permeability, especially vertically, which permits free flow of water from the ground surface to the water table. There has also been an increase in horizontal permeability, mainly through steeply inclined fractures oriented transverse to the direction of slide movement.

Structures affecting ground-water movement

The main structural features of the peninsula include the northwesterly trending doubly plunging anticline along the crest of the peninsula, and the Palos Verdes fault on the north side of the peninsula (Fig. 1). In general, ground-water flow on the southern flank of the doubly plunging anticline is toward the southwest.

In the vicinity of the Abalone Cove landslide the Portuguese Tuff serves as an effective barrier to vertically downward ground-water movement. The ground-water basin and the ancient landslide complex have approximately the same boundaries. Both are strongly influenced by the base of the Portuguese Tuff.

The scarp along the head of the Abalone Cove landslide joins a graben area in the Portuguese Bend landslide. Ground-water movement in the northeastern part of the Abalone Cove landslide is dependent on the elevation of the water table in both

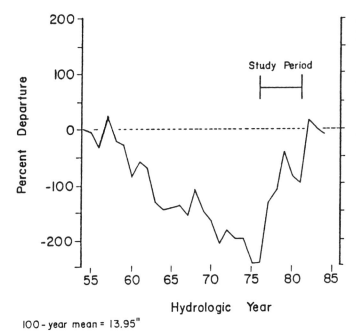

Figure 4. Cumulative departure from mean rainfall at Los Angeles County Flood Control Station 1011B.

of the landslides, and can be either into, or out of, the Abalone Cove landslide. Within the Abalone Cove landslide, ground-water flow is predominately in a southerly direction; however, low permeability listric normal faults oriented generally east-west hold the ground water in compartments, and cause a stepping down of the water table to the south.

Ground water is present primarily above the active slide plane and flows through the disturbed materials, which are found above the active slide plane. In some places this pattern of circulation is confirmed by abundant iron oxide (hematite) above the active slide plane and unoxidized iron sulfide (pyrite) below the slide plane. The black or gray undisturbed bedrock below the active slide plane generally has a low permeability. No zones of ground water under a pressure head have been found beneath the active slide plane.

LANDSLIDE MOVEMENT

Landslide movement has been significantly greater to the south of Palos Verdes Drive South than to the north, as shown by the displacements of the Los Angeles County surveying monuments. Monument Q-2, located within the county beach property (Fig. 3), moved 4.9 ft (1.47 m) horizontally between 1957, when the point was established, and November 15, 1977, when the monument was first resurveyed. Most of this movement probably occurred between 1974 and 1977. This point (Q-2) showed 29.1 ft (0.87 m) of horizontal displacement and −3.5 ft (−0.10 m) of vertical displacement during the period November 15, 1977, to January 5, 1985. Los Angeles County Survey point P-2A, lo-

cated along Palos Verdes Drive South (Fig. 3), was displaced horizontally 20.1 ft (0.60 m) during the period from February 10, 1976, to January 5, 1985.

In November 1978, Perry Ehlig and I established monitoring stations. Locations of some of these stations are indicated in Figure 3.

Effects of water on slide stability

There is a strong direct correlation between landslide movement and ground-water levels. Figure 3 indicates the location of dewatering and monitoring wells within and immediately upslope of the Abalone Cove landslide. The Abalone Cove landslide began slowing immediately after the start of dewatering operations began in March 1980 (Figs. 6 and 7). Figure 6 shows the relation between the water level at WW-5, the rate of displacement at Monitoring Station 1, the water level at monitoring well Sweetbay West (located 1200 ft [360 m] upslope from the head of the active slide), and rainfall. As the water table rose at WW-5, prior to the initiation of dewatering, the rate of landslide displacement increased, and as the water table fell during dewatering, the rate of displacement decreased. Note the strong correlation between the start of dewatering and the decline in the water table at WW-5 and the decrease in the rate of landslide movement at Monitoring Station 1, even though the water table was still rising beneath the stable area upslope of the landslide. Figure 7 illustrates the relation between the rate of movement at Monitoring Station 2 and the water level at monitoring well Wayfarer East, which is 400 ft (120 m) downslope from Monitoring Station 2. Note the increase in landslide movement at Monitoring Station 2 while upslope dewatering well WW-7 was out of order.

Relations between rainfall and groundwater

Rainfall has both an immediate and a delayed effect on ground-water conditions. The 1980–1981 hydrologic year, as recorded at Los Angeles County Flood Control (LACFC) Station 1011B (Fig. 5), was drier than normal (Table 1). Only 7.77 in (~19.75 cm) of precipitation was recorded. This amount, however, was sufficient to cause movement to accelerate within the Abalone Cove landslide. The 3.24 in (~8.23 cm) that fell during the eight day period from February 26, 1981, through March 5, 1981 (as recorded at LACFC Station 1011B), was enough to cause the water table to rise 1.8 ft (0.54 m) at WW-5 and cause a brief resumption of movement at Monitoring Station 1 (Fig. 6).

The fairly rapid rise of the water table within the active landslide is due to open fissures that conduct runoff directly to the water table during periods of heavy runoff (see Fig. 6 for changes in water-table levels following periods of heavy rainfall). During periods of heavy rainfall, one could see runoff from streets and culverts disappear into fissures. Monitoring well Wayfarer East is about 200 ft (60 m) downslope from a major fissure that received runoff from Narcissa Drive by way of a culvert. During a nine day rainy period in February 1980, 9.28 in (~23.6 cm) of precip-

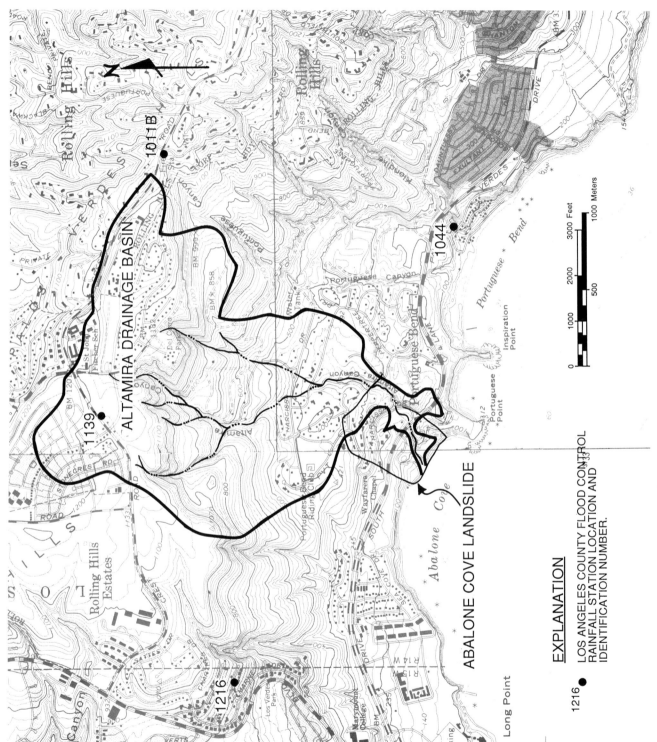

Figure 5. Boundaries of Altamira drainage basin.

EXPLANATION

● LOS ANGELES COUNTY FLOOD CONTROL
1216   RAINFALL STATION LOCATION AND
       IDENTIFICATION NUMBER.

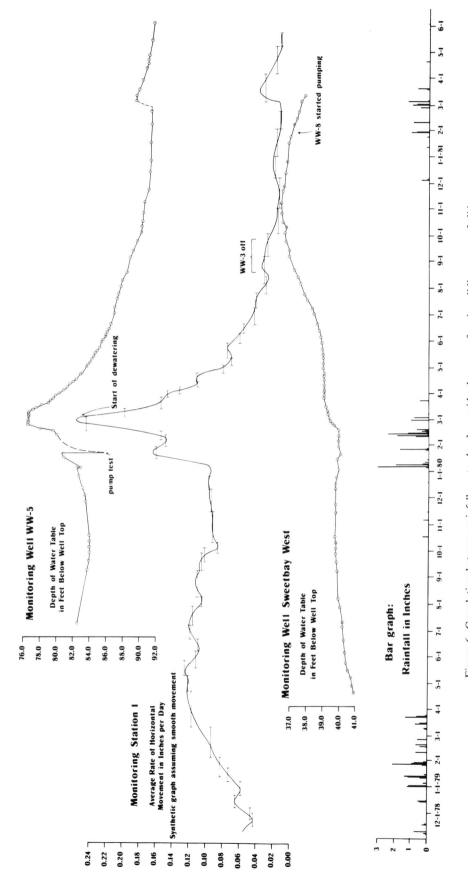

Figure 6. Correlation between rainfall, water levels outside the area of active sliding, rates of slide movement, and water levels within the active landslide.

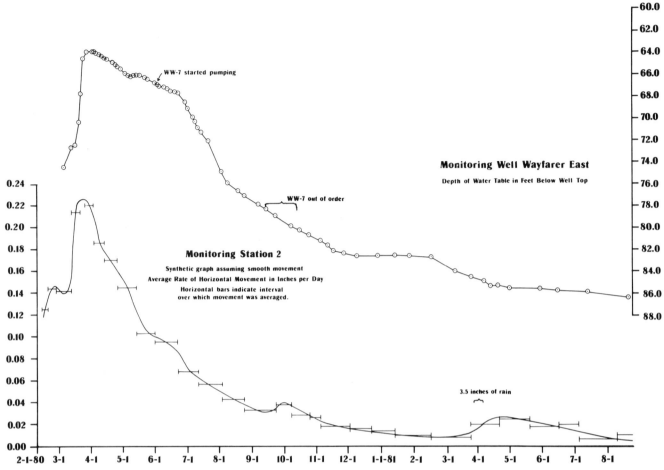

Figure 7. Correlation between water levels at Monitoring Well Wayfarers East and movement rates at Monitoring Station 2 for the period February–March 1980 to August 1981.

itation was recorded at LACFC Station 1011B. This rainfall caused the water table to rise 8.83 ft (2.65 m) at Wayfarer East in a 17 day period (Fig. 7).

In areas upslope from the active landslide, fluctuations in the water table elevation are very gradual. MW-Sweetbay West is a monitoring well located outside the area of active sliding, and until January 30, 1981, was outside the area of dewatering. Water-level records for this well began on April 19, 1979. As shown in Figure 6, there appears to be a one to one and one-half month delay between the first period of heavy winter rainfall and the first measured rise in the water table at this well (measurements are taken on average every six days). The full impact of a rainy season on the water table at this well is not experienced for eight to nine months after precipitation stops. Thus the full effect of rainfall during February and March does not occur until October or November. A similar pattern was noted from water-level monitoring data collected at WW-1. Water-level data were collected at WW-1 from July 1979 to March 1980, before dewatering operations began. The water level was highest in late summer and then declined in fall and early winter.

GROUND-WATER SUPPLY, MOVEMENT, AND STORAGE

Ground-water supply

Water is supplied to the ground-water body by way of deep percolation of surface inflow, precipitation, delivered water, and subsurface inflow.

Percolation of surface inflow. The major source of surface inflow is runoff of precipitation from upslope areas. Other sources of surface inflow are insignificant. The acreage of the upslope area being drained, and the location where runoff enters the landslide are as follows: 781 acres (~312 ha) enter along the head of the landslide, 5.19 acres (~2.1 ha) enter along the east boundary, and 21.34 (~8.5 ha) along the west boundary.

Rainfall runoff depends upon the rate of rainfall infiltration, which in turn depends upon the type of soil and the intensity of the storm (how many inches fell within a period of time). The Los Angeles County Flood Control District (LACFCD) has published infiltration rates for the soil types present within the Altamira drainage basin (LACFCD, 1971).

TABLE 1. RECORDED RAINFALL IN INCHES AND PERCENT OF NORMAL RAINFALL AT LOS ANGELES COUNTY FLOOD-CONTROL STATIONS 1011A AND 1011B

Hydrologic year	Rainfall	Percent of normal*	95% of rainfall	84% of rainfall
1011A				
1949–1950	11.11	80	10.55	9.33
1950–1951	10.01	72	9.51	8.41
1951–1952	23.36	167	22.19	19.62
1952–1953	10.53	74	9.85	8.71
1953–1954	13.45	96	12.78	11.30
1954–1955	9.16†	66	8.70	7.69
1011B				
1955–1956	13.18	94	12.52	10.07
1956–1957	10.11	72	9.60	8.49
1957–1958	21.61	155	20.53	18.15
1958–1959	7.78	56	7.39	6.54
1959–1960	12.95	93	12.30	10.88
1960–1961	5.53	40	5.25	4.65
1961–1962	18.21	131	17.30	15.30
1962–1963	11.90	85	11.31	10.00
1963–1964	6.01	43	5.71	5.05
1964–1965	11.86	85	11.27	9.96
1965–1966	14.39	103	13.67	12.09
1966–1967	14.38	103	13.66	12.08
1967–1968	11.26	81	10.70	9.46
1968–1969	20.87	150	19.83	17.53
1969–1970	8.36	60	7.94	7.02
1970–1971	11.42	82	10.85	9.59
1971–1972	8.05	58	7.65	6.76
1972–1973	17.59	126	16.71	14.78
1973–1974	11.75	84	11.16	9.87
1974–1975	14.31	103	13.59	12.02
1975–1976	7.41	53	7.04	6.22
1976–1977§	14.26	102	13.55	11.98
1977–1978§	28.43	204	27.01	23.88
1978–1979§	17.41	125	16.54	14.62
1979–1980§	23.85	171	22.66	20.03
1980–1981§	7.77	56	7.38	6.53
1981–1982§	12.21	88	11.60	10.26
1982–1983	30.24	217	28.73	25.40
1983–1984	11.29	81	10.73	9.48
1984–1985	12.49	90	11.87	10.49

*The 100-year normal for station 1011B is 13.95 inches as reported by Los Angeles County Flood Control Rainfall Division (personal communication, 1985).
†Rainfall value listed for the 1954–1955 season was estimated by the author using rainfall data from nearby stations.
§Rainfall data used in this chapter.

Continuous rainfall recording gauges are necessary to estimate the intensity of each of the storms and the amount of infiltration and runoff. The nearest continuous rainfall recorder is located at LACFCD station 444F-E, 3 mi (4.8 km) northeast of Abalone Cove. The total estimated percolation of surface inflow is listed in Table 2.

Percolation of rainfall. Rainfall within the Abalone Cove landslide and within the Altamira drainage basin below an eleva-

tion of 500 ft (150 m) is estimated to be 84% of the rainfall at LACFCD station 1011B (Ehlig, 1986) (Table 1). The computed 100 year mean annual precipitation at this station is 13.95 in (~35.43 cm) (LACFCD, 1985, personal commun.).

Rainfall at the site (1) leaves the site as runoff, (2) percolates and remains in the soil belt to be evaporated or used by the vegetation, or (3) percolates to the ground-water body. Runoff, as discussed in the previous section, depends upon the rate of rainfall infiltration, which depends upon the type of soil and the intensity of the storm.

In the developed and undeveloped parts of the landslide, rainfall that does not leave the area as runoff and that is in excess of the water needs of the vegetation percolates to the ground-water body. Percolation of rainfall was estimated by calculating the evapotranspiration water demand of the native grass in the undeveloped parts of the landslide and the landscaping in the developed parts of the landslide. Rainfall landing on low permeability surfaces such as asphalt, concrete, or roofing materials either reached the ocean as runoff or was added to the ground-water body after flowing down fractures and fissures or being ponded. The total estimated percolation of rainfall is listed in Table 2.

Percolation of delivered water. Deep percolation of delivered water includes percolation of system losses (water resulting from leaks or breaks in the water mains), sewage, and applied water (landscape watering). For the analysis of percolation of delivered water, water-supply records for the Abalone Cove area (108 water users) were obtained for the 5 year period from January 1975 through December 1979, as well as the period from January 1980 to December 1982, for three of the major water users.

System losses were estimated by noting water use that was abnormally high for a particular water user during a particular month. Water use is considered abnormally high when it exceeds 10,000 ft^3 (300 m^3) and exceeds twice the average water use. The system loss was estimated by subtracting the average water use for that particular month (during the period of record) from the recorded abnormally high water usage. The resulting remainder is considered the system loss. Estimated system losses are listed in Table 2. Water mains within the Abalone Cove landslide were put above ground surface in April 1980. It is assumed that any system losses after that time were noted and corrected before any significant amount of water had a chance to percolate to the ground-water table.

Water users within the Abalone Cove area use on-site sewage disposal systems (for example, cesspools, steepage pits, and leach fields). There are 25 water users within the Abalone Cove landslide area; 22 of these can be classified as single-family residences. Water users such as the Wayfarers Chapel, irrigated farming property, and any estates have been excluded from the single-family residence classification. The average monthly water usage of the 25 water users ranged from 1.52 acre feet in January to 3.82 acre feet in June (Ehlig, 1986). The average annual amount of water delivered to the 22 single-family residences

K. A. Proffer

**TABLE 2. ESTIMATED SUPPLY IN ACRE FEET TO THE ZONE OF SATURATION
WITHIN THE ABALONE COVE LANDSLIDE**

Water year	Percolation of surface inflow	Percolation of rainfall	Supply				Subsurface inflow	Total inflow
			Percolation System losses	of Delivered Water Sewage	Applied water		
1976–1977	2.4	16.6	1.7	9.2	6.2	39.8	75.9
1977–1978	5.6	90.3	3.1	9.1	1.9	39.8	149.8
1978–1979	8.9	24.3	2.4	9.1	3.7	39.8	88.2
1979–1980	18.6	73.4	....	8.5	3.8	39.8	144.1
1980–1981	0.9	9.4	....	9.0	1.4	39.8	60.5
1981–1982	3.1	16.3	....	8.5	1.9	39.8	69.6

(minus system losses) was 17.83 acre feet, or 724 gal (2751 l) per day per residence. The amount of water that is available for deep percolation (here after referred to as "waste water") is estimated to be 99% of the delivered water used during the months of January, February, and March of 1978 and January of 1979. During each of these months rainfall exceeded 5 in (12.7 cm). It is therefore assumed that essentially all of the delivered water was used indoors (Linaweaver and others, 1967) and hence delivered to the sewage system. Waste water, as estimated above, is 37% of the average annual net delivered water. This means that an average of 6.66 acre feet per year is contributed to the ground-water body by the 22 residences, or 270 gal (1026 l) per day per residence.

It is estimated that water users other than single-family residences contribute on the average 3.32 acre feet of water per year to the ground-water body within the Abalone Cove landslide (987 gal [3,750 l] per day per water user). These values were calculated assuming that 99% of the delivered water during the months of January, February, and March of 1978, and January of 1979, were disposed of as waste water. This estimated waste water is 25% of the average annual net delivered water to these water users. Delivered water use was evaluated on a month by month basis. During some of the months no water was delivered to a water user, or an abnormally low amount, which was most likely used for landscape watering. The estimated amount of water percolating to the ground-water table as waste water was adjusted appropriately.

All delivered water not becoming sewage (waste water) is assumed to have been used outside the home (applied water). The amount of water that is added to the ground-water body by way of deep percolation of applied water was estimated taking into account rainfall, evapotranspiration of the vegetation, and surface inflow. Evapotranspiration rates for the existing vegetation were approximated using the method presented by MacGillivray in California Department of Water Resources (CDWR) (1975).

Subsurface inflow. Ground water enters the Abalone Cove landslide along the northern boundary (head) of the landslide. It is likely that one or more shear planes at the head of the slide result in one or more low-permeability barriers. Clay gouge

is likely to be present along the shear planes due to the high clay content of the ancient landslide material. The predominant rock materials in the zone of saturation at the head of the landslide are, in order of abundance, clay, cherty shale, thickly bedded to laminated cherty dolomite, and cherty or dolomitic siltstone (as encountered during the drilling of WW-3, WW-4, WW-7, WW-6, and MW—6A) (Robert Stone & Associates, 1980a, 1980b). Localized fracturing of the landslide debris along the head of the slide results in highly variable permeabilities. Open cavities were encountered 130–138 ft (39–41.4 m) below ground surface (28–36 ft (8.4–10.8 m) below the water table) during the drilling of WW-7. Fracture surfaces exposed to ground water are commonly coated by black manganese dioxide or reddish-brown iron oxide. Such surfaces were noted at a depth of 142–146 ft (42.6–43.8 m) in WW-7, and 130–138 ft (39–41.4 m) and 150–158 ft (45–47.4 m) in WW-3, as well as in other wells. Due to these conditions, which result in highly variable permeabilities, transmissivity across the head of the landslide was estimated by the following method.

Subsurface inflow was estimated based on well production at dewatering wells WW-3, WW-4, and WW-7. Average annual production from these wells following a year of essentially normal rainfall is 40.49 acre feet (Ehlig, 1986). Percolation of delivered water from three residences, percolation of rainfall at these residences, and percolation of rainfall that landed on about 5 acres (2 ha) covered by native vegetation probably contribute to this production. The sum of these contributions is estimated to be 1.78 acre feet. Some of the subsurface inflow probably reaches WW-2. This portion of the subsurface inflow is estimated to be equivalent to one-quarter of the average annual production at WW-7 following a year of normal or less than normal rainfall (1.07 acre feet). With these adjustments, it is estimated that subsurface inflow is 39.8 acre feet per year. This amount is equivalent to a hydraulic conductivity of 3.0 gal (11.4 l) per day per square foot, assuming a hydraulic gradient of 0.19, a saturated thickness of 29 ft (8.7 m), and inflow along a width of 2,150 ft (645 m). For comparison, a hydraulic conductivity of 3 gal (11.4 l) per day per square foot would be expected for an unconsolidated deposit of sandy silt, silt loess, or glacial till (Freeze and

Cherry, 1979). Subsurface inflow would increase from the above estimated value if the hydraulic gradient is steepened or if the saturated thickness increased.

Subsurface inflow and outflow is possible along the head graben, which connects the Abalone Cove and Portuguese Bend landslides. The amount of inflow and outflow is considered negligible because the ground-water gradient between the areas is so low.

Ground-water movement from the zone of saturation

Pumpage. Four dewatering wells (WW-2, WW-3, WW-4 and WW-7) removed ground water from within the Abalone Cove landslide during the period of study. Three dewatering wells (WW-1, WW-6, and WW-8) removed ground water from the area upslope of the landslide during the same period. Data on the extraction of ground water from the initiation of dewatering in 1980 to September 30, 1982, are presented in Table 3. Since September 30, 1982, are presented in Table 3. Since September 30, 1982, additional dewatering wells have been added to the system within and upslope of the landslide.

Evapotranspiration. Evapotranspiration is the water that evaporites directly from wet areas, including moist soil, or is transpired by plants. Of concern here is the loss of water from the ground-water body. Most of the vegetation within the Abalone Cove landslide and the Altamira drainage basin are shallowly rooted and obtain their water supply from either precipitation or yard watering. However, the pepper trees and other large trees within the landslide have roots that either intercept water in the intermediate zone or remove water from the saturated zone.

Evapotranspiration of the pepper trees and other large trees was approximated using the Blaney-Criddle method (Blaney and Criddle, 1962). The evapotranspiration of orange trees in coastal California, using the average monthly temperatures as recorded at Los Angeles International Airport, is considered representative of the pepper trees and other large trees. The area covered by these trees is ~5% of the landslides surface area, or 3.95 acres (1.58 ha). The estimated evapotranspiration is listed in Table 4.

Discharge to surface. Seeps in the beach area along the eastern half of the toe of the landslide, at about the high-tide level, were first noted about February 1982, following heavy wave erosion that had removed ~5 vertical ft (1.5 m) of beach gravel deposits. This erosion exposed upthrust slide debris composed of fractured to highly sheared shale overlain by fractured basalt. During later visits to this part of the beach, it was noted that the amount of seepage was greatest during years of heavy rainfall and those years which immediately followed years of heavy rainfall, but declined during drier years. Glenn Brown (LeRoy Crandall & Associates, May 1982, personal commun.), stated that members of his staff had recently approximated the seepage at that location to be 20 gal (76 l) per minute. Additional seeps are likely to be present along the part of the eastern half of the landslide toe, which is still covered by a gravel deposit. In addition, basalt crops

out in the surf zone in the east-central part of the landslide toe. Fractures in the basalt may provide excellent conduits for ground-water movement, as has been noted in the ground-water production at well WW-1, which removes ground water from fractured basalt. This information was used to arrive at the estimates listed in Table 4.

Subsurface outflow. A small amount of ground water exits at the toe of the landslide as subsurface outflow. This water flows through the clay gouge and landslide debris at the toe of the landslide into the marine sediments in Abalone Cove. The subsurface outflow was estimated using Darcy's Law, $Q = KIA$, where Q = discharge, K = hydraulic conductivity, I = hydraulic gradient, and A = cross-sectional area perpendicular to flow direction. The hydraulic conductivity used in the calculation of subsurface outflow is that which was approximated in the section on subsurface inflow, 3 gal (11.4 l) per day per square foot. The toe of the landslide was divided into three segments on the basis of changes in hydraulic gradient. The total average subsurface outflow is estimated to be 1.7 acre feet per year. This is a reasonable value for a year following a year of average or less than average rainfall. A steepening of the hydraulic gradient (a rise in water levels near the beach) results in greater subsurface outflow. Correspondingly, a gentler hydraulic gradient would result in less subsurface outflow.

Change in storage

In a ground-water basin, the difference between the inflow and the outflow of water is called the "change in storage." This annual amount can be computed in two ways: first the inventory method, where all inputs and outputs are summed and the difference is the change in storage; and second, the specific yield method, where the volume of the water added or lost as water levels in the basin rise or fall is computed. The latter method is considered more accurate. The results of both methods are listed in Table 4.

To compute the change in storage using the specific yield method, a water-table contour map and an isopach map of the saturated zone were prepared (Ehlig, 1986). No water-level information is available for hydrologic years 1976–1975 and 1977–1978. Based on the available data, the annual change in storage was estimated using a specific yield of 7% for the landslide material. A comparison of the estimated change in storage using the two methods reveals a maximum discrepancy of 0.6 acre feet (Table 4).

GROUND-WATER QUALITY

Ground-water samples were collected on both November 12, 1982, and May 4, 1983. These samples were analyzed by the Smith-Emery Company in Los Angeles.

The amount of total dissolved solids in the water samples ranged from 3431.0 parts per million (ppm) (WW-6 on May 4, 1983) to 4864.5 ppm (WW—7 on November 12, 1982). This

K. A. Proffer

TABLE 3. QUARTERLY WATER-WELL PRODUCTION STATISTICS

Well	Starting Date	Start to 7/30/80	7/30/80 to 10/5/80	10/5/80 to 1/9/81	1/9/81 to 3/31/81	3/31/81 to 7/8/81	7/8/81 to 10/10/81	10/10/81 to 1/7/82	1/7/82 to 4/6/82	4/6/82 to 7/2/82	7/2/82 to 10/7/82	Total Since Start
A. Production in Gallons												
WW-1	3/3/80	4,491,200	2,871,900	2,875,100	2,240,100[*]	2,924,900[*]	3,140,000	2,792,300	1,054,345[*,***,‡]	2,378,600	1,190,859[***]	25,959,304
WW-2	3/3/80	1,892,900	627,900	483,000	266,600	292,500	208,000	175,900	184,650	172,450	90,216[***]	4,394,116
WW-3	3/5/80	3,494,050	1,732,950[*,†]	4,351,000	3,786,700[*]	4,264,700[*]	3,778,100[*]	3,759,560	1,836,844[*,***]	464,590[*]	1,522,690[*]	28,991,184
WW-4	5/14/80	1,114,865	1,468,955	1,218,760	935,160	908,840	744,000	1,190,860	676,204[*,†††]	605,680	574,660	9,437,984
WW-6	4/25/80	644,650	457,870	434,480	557,660	575,140	755,500[*,§§]	664,360	300,815	441,550	339,750	5,171,775
WW-7	4/25/80	1,913,586	752,904[§]	730,050[§]	492,270	560,030	490,800	460,400	448,040	417,270	489,350	6,754,700
WW-8	1/30/81	....	....	....	318,980	322,420	260,480	231,600	208,120	206,545	186,705	1,734,850
Total Production		13,551,251	7,912,479	10,092,390	8,597,470	9,848,530	9,376,880	9,274,980	4,709,018	4,686,685	4,394,230	82,443,913
B. Average Production in Gallons per Day												
WW-1	3/3/80	36,813	30,552	29,949	27,656	29,544	33,053	31,374	11,847	27,340	12,277	27,211
WW-2	3/3/80	15,516	6,680	5,031	3,291	2,955	2,189	1,976	2,075	1,982	930	4,606
WW-3	3/5/80	29,117	18,436	45,323	46,749	43,078	39,769	42,242	20,639	5,340	15,698	30,453
WW-4	5/14/80	22,297	15,627	12,695	11,545	9,180	7,832	13,380	7,598	6,962	5,924	10,774
WW-6	4/25/80	9,343	4,871	4,526	6,885	5,584	7,953	7,465	3,380	5,075	3,503	5,779
WW-7	4/25/80	27,733	8,010	7.605	6,077	5,437	5,166	5,173	5,034	4,796	5,045	7,547
WW-8	1/30/81	....	....	....	5,316	3,257	2,742	2,602	2,338	2,374	1,925	2,821
Total Daily Average		140,819	84,176	105,129	107,519	99,035	98,704	104,212	52,911	53,869	45,302	89,191
C. Electrical Energy Consumption in Kilowatt Hours												
WW-1	3/3/80	4,341	2,769	2,899	2,312	2,562	2,435	2,316	1,919	1,714	1,602	24,869
WW-2	3/3/80	2,004	949	782	356	451	369	308	290	268	301	6,078
WW-3	3/5/80	4,785[**]	3,147	3,368	2,778	3,881	3,257	3,241	3,719	2,713	2,449	33,338
WW-4	5/14/80	1,272	1,926	1,417	1,156	1,293	1,065	1,832	1,004	724	672	12,361
WW-6	4/25/80	918	1,164	1,063	837	1,359	1,447	977	952	556	644	9,917
WW-7	4/25/80	2,421	1,072	1,077	810	657	839	601	690	654	545	9,366
WW-8	1/30/81	....	....	....	637	896	718	498	274	298	326	3,647
Total Consumption		15,741	11,027	10,606	8,886	11,099	10,130	9,773	8,848	6,927	6,539	99,576
Production Efficiency in Gallons per Kilowatt Hour												
WW-1	3/3/80	1,035	1,037	992	969	1,142	1,290	1,206	549	1,388	743	1,044
WW-2	3/3/80	945	662	618	749	649	564	571	637	643	300	723
WW-3	3/5/80	730	551	1,292	1,363	1,099	1,160	1,160	494	171	622	870
WW-4	5/14/80	876	763	860	809	703	699	650	674	837	855	764
WW-6	4/25/80	702	393	409	666	423	522	680	316	794	528	522
WW-7	4/25/80	709	702	678	608	852	585	766	649	638	898	721
WW-8	1/30/81	....	....	....	501	360	363	465	760	693	573	476
All Wells		861	718	952	968	887	926	949	532	677	672	828

[*]Water meter inoperative during part of period; production extrapolated from power consumption.
[†]WW-3 out of order from 8/20/80 to 9/26/80; turbine pump replaced by submersible pump.
[§]WW-7 out of order from 9/13/80 to 10/15/80; turbine pump replaced by submersible pump.
[**]Used meter; start reading extrapolated.
[‡]WW-1 out of order 3/10/82 to 3/22/82.
[§§]WW-6 out of order from 9/12/81 to 9/21/81; turbine pump replaced by submersible pump.
[***]New meter installed.
[†††]WW-4 out of order 3/10/82 to 3/20/82.

water is unfit for human consumption due to the high concentration of total dissolved solids (Hem, 1970). It is also unfit for human consumption because of the sulfate, chloride, nitrate, and iron ion concentrations. The predominant cations are sodium and magnesium and the predominant anion is sulfate (Fig. 8). The major constituents of the ground-water samples reflect the marine sedimentary depositional environment of the bedrock.

CONCLUSIONS AND RECOMMENDATIONS

Conclusions

These conclusions refer to hydrologic years 1976–1977 through 1981–1982. Both the first and last years had nearly average rainfall. During those years recharge into the Abalone

TABLE 4. ESTIMATED HISTORICAL DEEP PERCOLATION TO AND FROM THE ZONE OF SATURATION IN ACRE-FEET, ABALONE COVE LANDSLIDE

Water year	Supply				Pumpage	Disposal			Change in storage inflow-outflow	Change in storage specific yield method
	Percolation of surface inflow	Percolation of rainfall	Percolation of delivered water	Subsurface inflow		Evapo-trans-piration	Discharge to surface	Subsurface outflow		
1976–1977	2.4	16.6	17.1	39.8	....	9.7	40.3	1.7	24.2	....
1977–1978	5.6	90.3	14.1	39.8	....	9.8	56.4	3.2	80.4	....
1978–1979	8.9	24.3	15.2	39.8	....	9.7	61.3	3.2	14.0	....
1979–1980	18.6	76.7	12.3	39.8	13.3	9.6	54.8	3.2	63.2	62.6
1980–1981	0.9	9.4	10.4	39.8	71.2	9.9	38.7	3.2	-62.5	-62.6
1981–1982	3.1	16.3	10.4	39.8	41.2	9.6	32.2	1.7	-15.1	-15.7

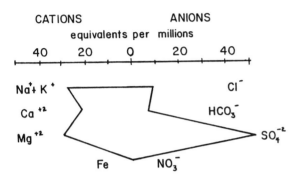

Figure 8. Stiff diagram of the major ground-water constituents at WW-4.

Cove landslide was about 73 acre feet, of which about 55% was subsurface inflow, 22% was percolation of rainfall, 19% was percolation of delivered water, and 4% was percolation of surface inflow. During years of abnormally high rainfall (1977–1978, 1979–1980), rainfall was about 147 acre-feet, of which about 56% was percolation of rainfall, 27% was subsurface inflow, 9% was percolation of delivered water, and 8% was percolation of surface inflow.

Prior to the start of the dewatering operations, the major source of ground-water disposal was discharge to the surface in the form of seeps along the toe of the landslide. This constituted about 81% of the ground-water disposal. Evapotranspiration and subsurface outflow accounted for about the remaining 15% and 4%, respectively. The dewatering system went on line on March 3, 1980. During the two years the dewatering system was fully operational (1980–1981, 1981–1982), pumpage constituted about 54% of the ground-water discharge, and discharge to the surface, evapotranspiration, and subsurface outflow constituted 34%, 9%, and 3%, respectively. During the first three years of the study period, recharge exceeded depletion, resulting in a net increase of about 118.6 acre feet in storage. During the last three years of the study period, discharge exceeded recharge, resulting in a net decrease in storage of about 14.4 acre feet. The dewatering system was very effective in removing ground water from the landslide.

Recommendations

On the basis of the above conclusions, the following strategy is recommended to minimize the ground-water supply and to maximize ground-water disposal.

1. A primary effort should be made to eliminate, or minimize, the amount of water available for subsurface inflow. The greatest source of water to the ground-water supply up gradient from the Abalone Cove landslide is probably percolation of rainfall in the undeveloped parts of the ancient landslide complex. Dewatering wells would be an effective way to remove this water. Three dewatering wells were added to the dewatering system upslope of the Abalone Cove landslide in 1985. These wells have added significantly to the removal of ground water in the Abalone Cove area. Another major source of ground water is the 76 water users upslope of the Abalone Cove landslide. They probably contribute 21.3 acre feet of water per year in the form of sewage. A sewer system, with export of sewage, would effectively eliminate this contribution.

2. During the wet years of 1977–1978 and 1979–1980, about 75% of the rainfall that percolated to the ground-water table fell in the undeveloped parts of the landslide itself. Measures to decrease the infiltration in these areas would most likely be uneconomical and esthetically undesirable. Thus, maintaining the dewatering system within the landslide should be continued.

3. Percolation of rainfall has increased since sliding started due to fissuring. Open cracks and fissures provide direct conduits for surface water to reach the ground-water table. All cracks and fissures should be sealed.

4. Percolation of sewage constitutes about 67% of the percolation of delivered water, whereas system losses constitutes 9% (the remaining 24% is percolation of applied water) (Tables 2 and 4). During the six year study period, the combined total of percolation of sewage and system losses contributed about 10% of the water supply to the ground-water body. Above-ground water supply lines and the installation of a sewer system should eliminate this source of supply.

5. Percolation of surface inflow and some (17% during the study period) of the percolation of rainfall can be eliminated with

the installation of a storm-drain system, the lining of Altamira channel, and the regrading of areas of ponding, resulting in proper drainage. Altamira channel has been lined from the head area of the landslide to the south side of Palos Verdes Drive South; however, improvement of surface drainage needs to be undertaken, so that the runoff and all surface inflow can reach the channel and be directed to the ocean.

6. The pepper trees and the other large trees are beneficial in the removal of subsurface water and should therefore be retained.

7. Operation of the dewatering system should continue. Six dewatering wells have been added to the dewatering system since September 1982. Five of these went on line in 1985; three of these are located within the Abalone Cove landslide. The additional wells have dramatically increased the production of the dewatering system and have contributed to the reduction of the landslide movement, which is near zero. The toe area stopped moving by September 1985.

ACKNOWLEDGMENTS

The results reported in this paper are part of a Master of Science thesis at California State University, Los Angeles. I thank Robert Bean, Martin Stout, and Perry Ehlig for their technical guidance and encouragement. WZI, Inc., provided assistance in preparation of illustrations. I thank James Slosson and anonymous reviewers for their comments and suggestions.

REFERENCES CITED

Blaney, H. F., and Criddle, W. D., 1962, Determining consumptive use and irrigation water requirements: U.S. Department of Agriculture Technical Bulletin 1275, p. 1–52.

California Department of Water Resources, 1975, Vegetative water use in California, 1974: California Department of Water Resources Bulletin 113-3, 104 p.

Conrad, C. L., 1983, Lithostratigraphy of the Monterey Formation of the Palos Verdes Peninsula, Los Angeles County, California [M.S. thesis]: Los Angeles, California State University, 96 p.

Ehlig, K. A., 1986, The hydrogeology of the Abalone Cove landslide, Rancho Palos Verdes, Los Angeles County, California [M.S. thesis]: Los Angeles, California State University, 121 p.

Freeze, R. A., and Cherry, J. A., 1979, Groundwater: Englewood Cliffs, New Jersey, Prentice-Hall, Inc., p. 29.

Hem, J. D., 1970, Study and interpretation of chemical characteristics of natural water (second edition): U.S. Geological Survey Water-Supply Paper 1473, p. 322.

Larue, D. K., 1976, The sedimentary response to landsliding in the marine nearshore, Portuguese Bend landslide complex, California [M.S. thesis]: Evanston, Illinois, Northwestern University, p. 7–9.

Lass, G. L., and Eagen, J. T., 1982, Introduction to the ancient Abalone Cove landslides, in Cooper, J. D., compiler, Landslides and landslide abatement, Palos Verdes Peninsula, southern California (Geological Society of America Cordilleran Section annual meeting guidebook): Association of Engineering Geologists, Southern California Section, p. 81–87.

Linaweaver, F. P., Jr., Geyer, J. C., and Wolff, J. B., 1967, A study of residential water use: Federal Housing Administration, Department of Housing and Urban Development, HUD TS-12, 94 p.

Los Angeles County Flood Control District, 1971, Hydrology manual: Los Angeles, California, Los Angeles County Flood Control District, Hydraulic Division, Figs. C-1.2, C-1.3, C-1.4, C-5.1, C-5.3, C-6.1.

Novak, G. A., 1982, Mineralogy and chemistry of bentonite from the Abalone Cove and Portuguese Bend landslids, southern California, in Cooper, J. D., compiler, Landslides and landslide abatement, Palos Verdes Peninsula, southern California (Geological Society of America Cordilleran Section annual meeting guidebook): Association of Engineering Geologists, Southern California Section, p. 27.

Robert Stone & Associates, Inc., 1979a, Final report, Geotechnical investigation of Abalone Cove landslide, Rancho Palos Verdes, Los Angeles County, California: Canoga Park, California, Robert Stone & Associates, Inc., consulting report, Project 1372-00, 86 p. (unpublished).

—— , 1979b, Dewatering test results and related analyses, Abalone Cove landslide, Rancho Palos Verdes, California: Canoga Park, California, Robert Stone & Associates, Inc., consulting report, Project 1372-98, 41 p. (unpublished).

—— , 1980a, First progress report on Abalone Cove landslide dewatering project: Canoga Park, California, Robert Stone & Associates, Inc., consulting report, Project 1546, 41 p. (unpublished).

—— , 1980b, Second progress report, Abalone Cove landslide dewatering project: Canoga Park, California, Robert Stone & Associates, Inc., consulting report, Project 1546-00, 33 p. (unpublished).

MANUSCRIPT ACCEPTED BY THE SOCIETY FEBRUARY 21, 1992

Geological Society of America
Reviews in Engineering Geology, Volume IX
1992

Chapter 9

Thistle landslide: Was mitigation possible?

James E. Slosson
Slosson and Associates, 15500 Erwin Street, Suite 1123, Van Nuys, California 91411
Delmar D. Yoakum
6634 Valjean Avenue, Van Nuys, California 91406
Gerard Shuirman
1426 Eastwind Circle, Westlake Village, California 91361

ABSTRACT

In April 1983, Spanish Fork Canyon, Utah, was engulfed by a massive landslide that dammed Spanish Fork Creek, creating a lake. The slide pushed and finally buried sections of the Denver & Rio Grande Western Railroad line and U.S. Highways 6, 50, and 89, which for decades had been located in Spanish Fork Canyon. When motion of this massive debris flow and/or landslide complex finally ceased, almost the entire 6,800-ft-long (2,040 m) and 800–1,100-ft-wide (240–330 m) mass, more than 200 ft (60 m) thick had moved. Spanish Fork Canyon, ~600 ft (180 m) wide at the location of the landslide, was filled to a depth of ~220 ft (66 m), causing a lake to form on the upstream side.

Data indicated that small displacements at the toe of the slide, adjacent to the Denver & Rio Grande Western Railroad, had been recorded since the early 1900s. Motion was correlative with years of above-average precipitation. Thus, the extraordinarily high precipitation of 1983, which was only ~2.2% higher than the previous record high precipitation of 1875–1876, added sufficiently to the ground-water regime to cause slow motion to develop in early April, followed by rapid acceleration in mid-April. Borings placed in 1984 indicated the existence of an artesian condition, the pressure level ranging from 25 to 65 ft (7.5 to 19.5 m) above ground surface near the toe of the slide. Other borings drilled at a later date provided samples from which strength parameters were determined. Test data indicate strength as low as 17.5° angle of internal friction and 210 lb/ft^2 cohesion.

Information obtained from all of these studies strongly suggests that had a surface-drainage system with horizontal (subsurface) drains been constructed prior to failure, landslide motion could have been prevented. Analyses indicate that a readily achievable lowering of the hydrostatic pressure on the slide planes would have produced a factor of safety greater than 1.0.

INTRODUCTION

Utah's wettest year in the past century was 1983; coming after the extremely wet year of 1982, the sequence created the wettest two-year cycle in the history of Utah. Storm conditions wrought havoc, causing extensive damage and record-breaking losses from landslides, debris flows and/or mudflows, and flood-

ing. Utah and the Salt Lake Valley and Wasatch Front have suffered from other record rain and snow, but property damage and financial losses were less, in part because of lower population figures and real property values.

Statistics indicate that above-average rainfall will occur in Utah approximately once in every 10 years. Fleming and Schuster (1985, p. 22) stated:

Slosson, J. E., Yoakum, D. D., and Shuirman, G., 1992, Thistle landslide: Was mitigation possible?, *in* Slosson, J. E., Keene, A. G., and Johnson, J. A., eds., Landslides/Landslide Mitigation: Boulder, Colorado, Geological Society of America Reviews in Engineering Geology, v. IX.

During 1983 . . . many large old landslides moved again . . . For most of these landslides, the only apparent cause of reactivation was an increase in subsurface water pressures resulting from the excessive precipitation. Unfortunately, critical data are lacking to predict (a) general groundwater response and, more importantly, (b) pore-pressure changes within the inactive landslide. . . .

It is very difficult to predict beforehand those landslides that are susceptible to reactivation by a change in subsurface water pressures. By careful mapping, the location of previously failed slopes can be identified (e.g., Shroder, 1971). It is also possible to infer the type and rate (within limits) of past movements from the landslide deposits and to measure the appropriate physical properties of the failed materials. The most critical unknown is the long-term behavior of water in the slope. Stabilities of slopes that are saturated to the ground surface differ by a factor of two from those of equivalent slopes in which the water table is located below the potential failure surface. In addition, certain geologic situations can result in groundwater conditions that produce even larger differences (Terzaghi, 1950). Piecemeal reactivation of portions of large landslides are also common; these can further complicate stability analysis.

Shroder (1967, 1971) mapped the location and geometry of the Thistle landslide and provided most of the basic geologic data. Ground-water data and strength parameters of the materials involved in previous slide activity were the only data lacking. The event in early 1983 became apparent to all on April 13, 1983, when the lower portion of the slide began to move. By late April 1983, almost the entire mass (in addition to some new materials from the headscarps) was in motion. Soon the slide became one of the largest active slides in the United States, causing some $200 million in losses (Fleming and Schuster, 1985). Kaliser and Fleming (1986) estimated the mass of landslide material in motion to be $\sim 22 \times 10^6$ m^3.

The slide moved across Spanish Fork Canyon, creating a natural dam ~ 200 ft (60 m) high. The body of water created by this natural dam blocked the Spanish Fork River, creating a lake with a depth, at the dam, approaching 200 ft (60 m). The volume of water impounded behind the dam was estimated to have exceeded 64,000 acre feet (8,000 ha-m). The lake inundated the community of Thistle, the Denver & Rio Grande Western Railroad and switch yards, as well as U.S. Highways 6, 50, and 89.

The landslide attained a length of more than 6,800 ft (2,040 m) and its thickness (or depth to the basal slide surface) ranged from 200 to 250 ft (60 to 75 m) (U.S. Geological Survey, I. Witkind and K. Murphy, 1983, unpublished field data) and possibly up to 350 ft (105 m) (our studies). We believe that more than 90% of the materials involved in this landslide had been involved in previous failures. The U.S. Geological Survey logs of borings indicate that the material involved in the landslide failure was the reactivation of ancient debris-flow material. We noted a deeper slide plane, ~ 100 ft (30 m) beneath the base of the older debris-flow material and within the underlying North Horn Formation. The width of the slide mass ranges from 700 ft (210 m) in the lower extremities to more than over 3,600 ft (1,080 m) in the

head scarp area. The majority of the slide varied in width from 900 to 1,100 ft (270–330 m).

THISTLE LANDSLIDE

On April 13, 1983, a large, youthful-looking landslide at Thistle, Utah, reactivated, developing within one day into one of the largest landslides of the western United States. Shroder (1967) mapped and discussed this landslide in detail and classified the Thistle landslide as ranging in geomorphic age from early youth to maturity. Shroder (1971) provided the following data related to the Thistle landslide (metric conversions in parentheses). Type of slide: complex slump and debris flow; dimensions: width—4,000 ft at head; 1,000 ft in middle; 900 ft at toe (1,200, 300, and 270 m, respectively); length—8,000 ft thick; 50 ft volume; 25 million yd^3 volume (2,400 m and 19 million m^3, respectively); elevation: crown—6,800 ft; head—6,500 ft; toe— 5,100 ft (2,040, 1,950, and 1,530 m, respectively); rate of movement: very rapid to slow; slope exposure: northeast; vegetation: sagebrush and scrub oak. Shroder (1971) also described the following. Geologic setting: conglomerate, sandstone, and red shale of the North Horn Formation of Cretaceous-Tertiary age, which is overlain by Tertiary limestone, shale and sandstone of the Flagstaff Formation and conglomerate and red beds of the Colton Formation, also of Tertiary age; causes of slide: poorly consolidated, argillaceous nature of the North Horn Formation; correlation: numerous slides have occurred, dating from late Pleistocene until very recently; and geomorphic age: early youth to maturity, as shown by successively younger slides headward.

This slide illustrates well repetitive or retrogressive movement. Continued instability in the head region is maintained by the formation of the main scarp after each episode of movement. Subsequent triggering effects produce successive landslides, each shorter and smaller than the preceding because of the reduction in slope and available unstable material.

Literature search provided information about other investigations that referred to the Thistle landslide and/or the general slope stability problems related to the slide and slopes in the vicinity. These references are as follows.

Peterson (1952, p. 2, 60, and 66, respectively) stated:

The main streams, though normally confined to their channels, become destructive torrents during periods of heavy rainfall as witnessed by damage during record flows in the spring of 1952.

Slumping is common on the steeper hillslopes. This phenomenon is particularly evident at the head of the basin west of Thistle.

As previously noted in the report some difficulty in describing certain formations and locating some contacts were experienced due mainly by slopewash. The area is generally undergoing active erosion. This is evidenced by gullying and normal stream erosion and by an unusual amount of slumping and sliding on certain steep slopes. The latter phenomenon is very pronounced near the head of the basin west of Thistle.

Rawson (1957, p. 3) noted:

Slumping is common on steeper hillsides, particularly in Spanish Fork Canyon and the railroad cut directly north of Thistle. West of the railroad cut, Tertiary sediments fill an ancient drainage channel in the Nugget sandstone. . . .During periods of heavy rains, slumping presents recurring problems of railroad clearance.

Rigby (1962, p. 81) noted:

Active creep of North Horn Flagstaff sediments through a gap in the Navajo Sandstone hogback north of Thistle, in Sec. 28, T.9S, R.4E, forms a hummocky slope area on the west side of the canyon. The highway was moved from the west to the east side of the canyon, in spite of obvious difficulties, because of the constant movement of the creep mass. The old highway grade can be seen ending against the rolling topography at the southern margin of the slide area.

Rigby (1968, p. 17) also made the following observation:

To the right, across Spanish Fork Canyon, can be seen a hummocky surface which is the result of creep and landslide of soft sedimentary rocks which overlie the tilted rocks of the canyon bottom. . . .The formations in the bottom dip upstream 15 to 20 degrees but the overlying formation is essentially horizontal. Additional evidence of this pronounced angular relationship, termed an angular conformity, can be seen upcanyon east of Thistle.

Rigby (1976, p. 5) stated:

The younger Tertiary rocks are soft and have flowed down into Spanish Fork Canyon on the south margin. This produced the hummocky rolling landscape visible above the railroad cuts in the sweeping bend of the canyon. A long tongue of landslide debris extends down through a gap in Navajo Sandstone on the west of the canyon 1.5 miles ahead, north of Thistle.

Other references or communication that contained valuable data are briefly noted, as follows.

D. S. Varnes classified the Thistle Landslide as active (1948, unpublished field notes). Varnes also stated that he had been informed of short, abrupt slide movements in the early 1940s. In addition, he noted that movement was related to rainfall. Kaliser (1984, oral commun.) stated that movement of the Thistle landslide has been documented over a period of years. His records showed that the Thistle landslide had moved essentially every winter and spring when there was significant, above average, rainfall and/or snow melt. Ozment (1983a, 1983b) stated that the first record of movement or slide at the toe of the Thistle landslide was in the early 1900s, and that the Denver & Rio Grande Western Railroad had removed several thousand cubic yards of landslide debris from the tracks in the 1950s. He also

remembered that the track had "humped-up" and moved east. His estimate of such movement was 5 ft (1.5 m) up and 3 ft (0.9 m) lateral (eastward). Ozment also noted that G. B. Aydelott, the previous division engineer, had informed him that similar types of movement had occurred in the 1940s and 1950s.

Relying on these references, other data, and field reconnaissance, it was apparent to us that the Thistle landslide was geomorphically youthful prior to the 1983 failure and fit the criteria necessary to be classified as an active landslide. Minor reactivation during the past century was adequate warning that large-scale reactivation was possible. Available data suggest that, had stability analysis been run prior to the April 13, 1983, failure, it would have been apparent that failure was imminent. Figure 1 shows the geology of the area as mapped by Witkind and Page (1983), Figure 2 shows the landslide as interpreted by us, and Figure 3 is a schematic cross-section of the slide before 1983.

After failure, many geologists and geotechnical engineers studied the landslide to determine the mode and cause of failure. Test borings drilled into the toe, lower, and middle parts of the landslide by Northern Engineering and Testing, Inc., in 1984 were available. These data included complete cores of borings, boring logs, piezometric records, tiltmeter data, and physical parameters determined by laboratory testing. We reviewed these data and selected Boring DH-8 as the best representation. From Boring DH-8, samples of slide plane or failure-surface materials were extracted and transported to the GeoSoils, Inc., laboratory in Van Nuys, California. Multiple samples were reviewed and samples from depths of 155 and 206 ft (~46.5 and 61.8 m) were tested. Both of these samples were of shear zones, the lower one being from within that portion of the boring that the U.S. Geological Survey (I. Witkind and K. Murphy, 1983, unpublished field notes) had logged as the base of the ancient debris flow and/or landslide. Slosson and Associates had picked slide planes at 155, 206, and 312 ft (~46.5, 61.8, and 93.6 m); however, suitable specimens were not available for testing from the zone of 312 ft. Visual inspection of the cores from DH-8 strongly suggests that the slide-plane gouge logged at –312 ft (~93.6 m) (subsurface) was as weak, if not weaker, than the materials at 206 ft (61.8 m).

The cores had been stored in a dry and sometimes hot building for months (December 1984 to July 1985) and thus were quite dry before we obtained them. Saturation of the samples for seven days under test confining loads brought the specimens to a moisture content somewhat below the suspected moisture content at the time of failure (April 1983). Thus, although some disturbance of the samples occurred through drying and rewetting, we believe that the test data show strength parameters that are higher than, but still reasonably representative, of strength parameters along the slide planes. Results of the tests were:

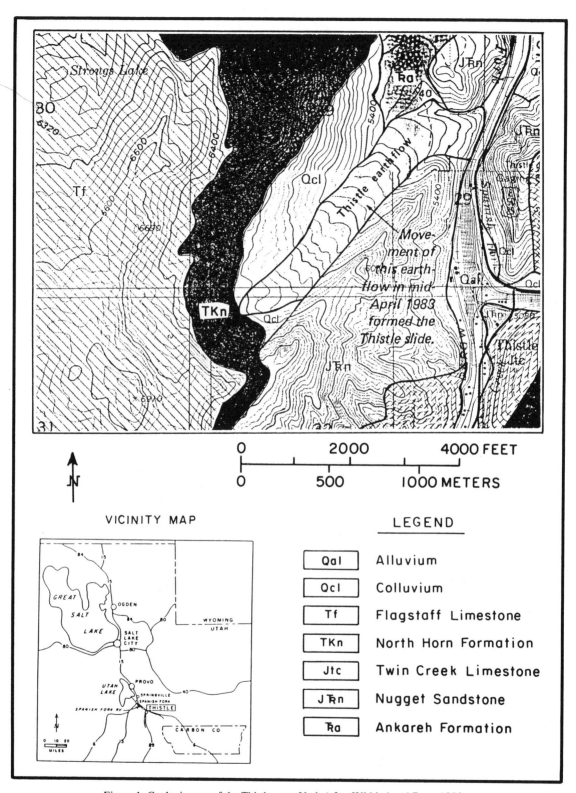

Figure 1. Geologic map of the Thistle area, Utah (after Witkind and Page, 1983).

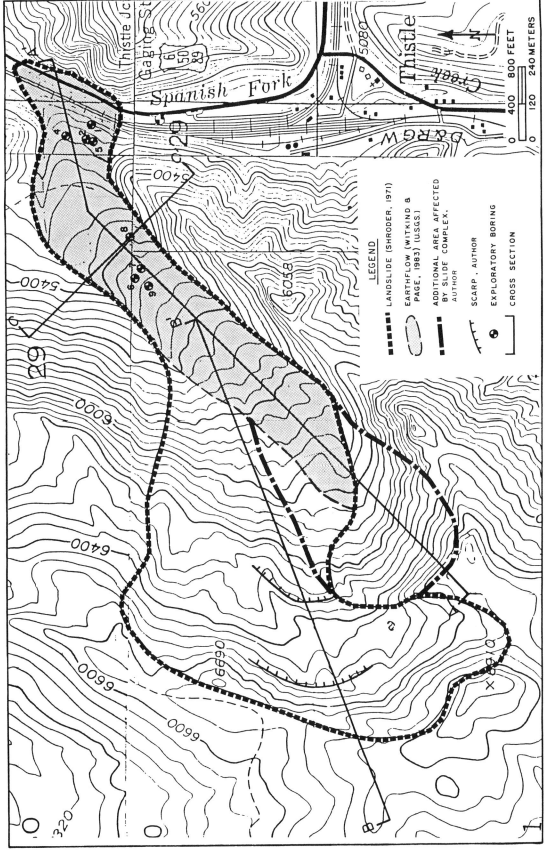

Figure 2. Landslide interpretation map of the Thistle area.

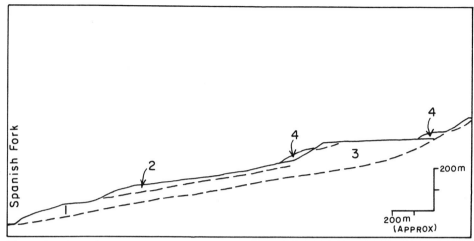

Figure 3. Schematic cross-section of Thistle landslide drawn nearly to scale. 1—first debris flow; 2—second debris flow; 3—slump block related to first or second debris flow, or both; 4—mudflows and debris flows of historic age (from Schroder, 1967).

Depth (ft)	Angle of internal friction (degrees)	Cohesion (psf)
155 (46.5 m)	17.5	480
206 (61.8 m)	22.0	210

Seepage issuing from the toe of the slide adjacent to the railroad tracks had been reported for years, so it was of interest to find, if possible, the piezometric head present in the slide mass and note if any variations existed. To identify hydrostatic pressures within the slide mass, Northern Engineering and Testing, Inc., installed multistaged piezometers in each of the borings as it was completed. The piezometers showed that there was a significant rise in the hydrostatic head in and near failure planes. More specifically, the general hydrostatic profile was well below the ground surface (10 to 80 ft; 3 to 24 m), but near the slide planes the hydrostatic head was found to be as much as 65 ft (19.5 m) above the ground surface (artesian condition). This specific phenomenon gave further verification that the deeper slide plane below 310 ft (93 m) was a valid active slide plane.

Simple slope-stability analyses were performed using the method of slices to determine the general range of factor of safety with varying hydrostatic heads on the assumed failure surface. These analyses used some simplifying assumptions, such as a uniform hydrostatic head on the assumed failure surface relative to the ground surface; however, the results, presented in Figure 4, simply verify what we already know, that failure was predictable with the preexisting conditions.

In our opinion, surface and subsurface drainage, as shown in Figures 5, 6, 7, and 8, could have provided adequate drainage to lower the water table and thus abate slide mobilization. Data obtained from piezometers installed by Northern Engineering and Testing, Inc., show that the piezometric head was as much as 65 ft (19.5 m) above ground surface and average at least 25 ft (7.5 m) above ground elevation in January 1985. Because these data were obtained from borings drilled after failure, it is reasonable to assume that the piezometric head was higher at the early stages of failure, prior to ground water exiting from the toe of the landslide as spring flow (before piezometric data were obtained).

The proposed surface drainage would have allowed rainfall and snow melt to flow rapidly to the Spanish Fork River, preventing ponding of water, such as in two small lakes at the head of the slide. Many shallow ponding areas existed prior to failure and many new low spots or ponds now exist. Surface ponding allows for extended periods of time for influent seepage and percolation to occur, which contributes to the ground-water regime.

Proposed subdrains would have allowed for exit of water from the slide mass, resulting in a lowering of the water table. Subdrains placed in somewhat similar materials have developed flows up to 50 gal/min (190 l) from the 2 in plastic pipe recommended.

Cost estimates for the surface drainage facilities range from $128,000 for construction of two unlined channels to $433,000 for gunited channels, grouted rock-drop structures, and compaction of excess dirt (or spoils) (Table 1).

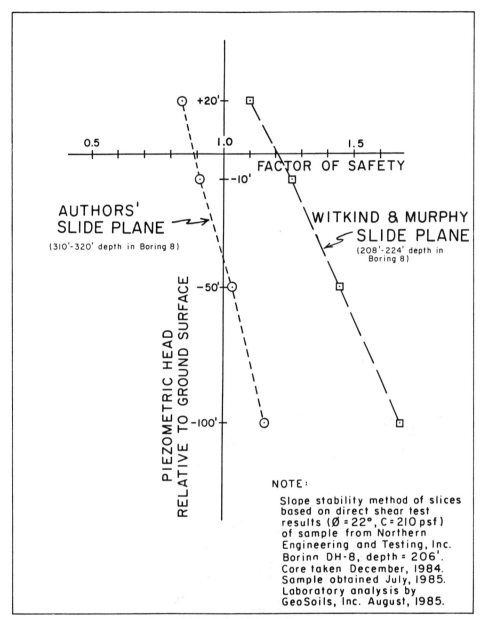

Figure 4. Thistle landslide stability analyses.

CROSS SECTION OF GUNITE DRAINAGE CHANNEL

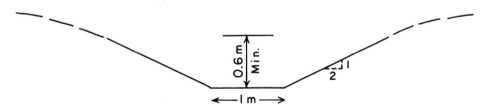

Figure 5. Cross-section of Gunite drainage channel.

TYPICAL PROFILE
GROUTED ROCK DROP STRUCTURE AND GRADIENT

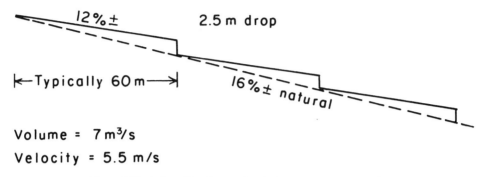

Figure 6. Typical profile of grouted rock drop structure and gradient.

CONCLUSIONS

The Thistle landslide had been recognized as a youthful (or active) landslide; its geometry had been determined and recorded by 1967, microactivity had been recorded from the turn of the century, and the general relation of precipitation to slide activity has been recognized by many. Data were obtainable by way of standard practice subsurface exploration, sampling, and testing (some were substantially obtained after failure) to determine the following: (1) the location of the post-slide activity hydrostatic pressures within the slide mass; (2) the effect of precipitation on the water table and ground-water regime; (3) the strength parameters for slide plane materials; and (4) the effect of the water table on the stability of the slide mass.

Analysis of these data indicated that a lowering of the water table by utilizing surface and subsurface drains would have prevented failure and would have mitigated the inherent landslide hazard except for minor slumping and/or sloughing at the toe. Cost of mitigation was estimated to range from ~$275,000 for temporary surface and subsurface drainage to control, to ~$550,000 for permanent (with maintenance) drainage.

The total cost of losses and reconstruction was about $200 million (Fleming and Schuster, 1985). Reconstruction of the rail system alone has been estimated to have cost more than $40 million.

A review of all of the pertinent data shows clearly that, with utilization of standard practice technology, the Thistle landslide was recognizable, predictable, and preventable. The cost benefit ratio to have mitigated the Thistle landslide would have been at least 1,000 to 1, or one thousand dollars saved for each dollar spent to mitigate.

Some have suggested that there are too many landslides to consider mitigation and that the cost would be prohibitive. On the basis of education and experience, it is our opinion that the hundreds of significant landslides could be studied easily and catalogued utilizing a classification methodology that would list landslides as moving (active); incipient; quasistable; stable in current environs; and stable unless major changes occur.

This cataloging would begin with a study of all available aerial photographs and topographic maps, which would provide the information needed to begin the assessment of the relative danger of the various landslides. On the basis of this initial overview study, it would be possible to determine which sites should be studied further by reconnaissance by air or foot; then the landslides determined to present the greatest hazards could be subject to a limited site analysis. In this way, the landslides found to be of greatest risk would receive the most available time and resources.

It can be assumed that slides classified as moving or incipient and that are located so as to pose an immediate hazard should be less than 10% of the total. From experience, the ratio of the cost of losses and reconstruction versus cost of mitigation should be in the range of 100 to 1. Similar cost ratios for case-history studies done by us range from 10 to 1 up to 2,000 to 1, always a savings of considerable money.

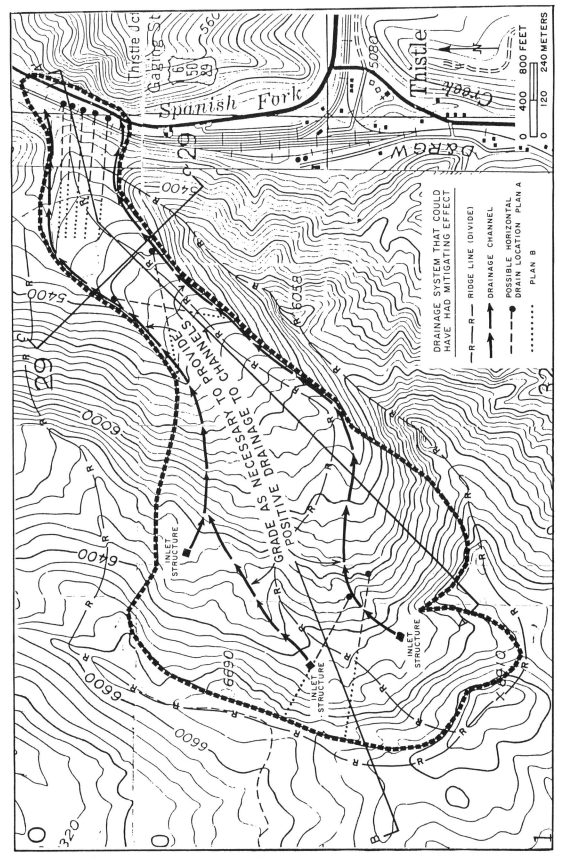

Figure 7. Drainage system that could have had mitigating effect.

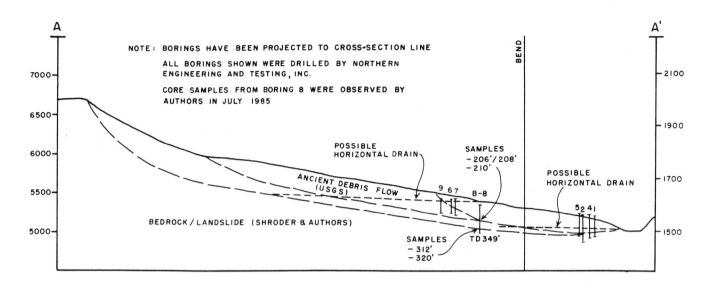

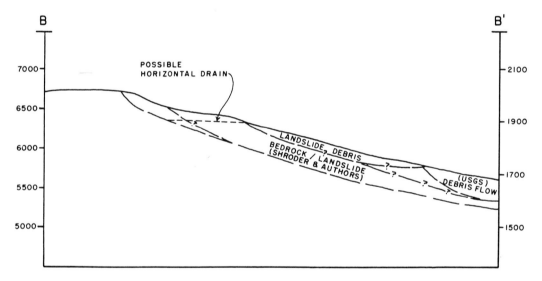

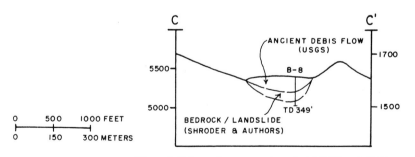

Figure 8. Schematic cross-sections A-A′, B-B′, and C-C′.

TABLE 1. COST ESTIMATE OF SURFACE DRAINAGE SYSTEM THAT COULD HAVE HAD MITIGATING EFFECT ON THE SLIDE

1. Two gunite drainage channels, total length ~14,000 linear ft

Clearing 280,000 ft² (25,200 m²) @ $0.10/ft²	$ 28,000
Excavation 20,000 yd³ (15,200 m³) @ $2.00/yd³	40,000
Spoil 20,000 yd³ (15,200 m³) @ $3.00/yd³	60,000
Ditching only	*$128,000*
Recompact 5,000 yd³ (3,800 m³) @ $5.00/yd³	25,000
Gunite 105,000 ft² (9,450 m²) @ $2.00/ft²	210,000
Subtotal	$363,000

2. Grouted Rock Drop Structures at average 200 foot (60 m) spacing:

70 feet (21 m) @ $1,000/ft	$ 70,000
Total	$433,000

REFERENCES CITED

Fleming, R. W., and Schuster, R. L., 1985, Implications of the current wet cycle to landsliding in Utah, *in* Proceedings of Specialty Conference, Utah State University, June 14–15, 1984: Utah State University, Utah Water Research Laboratory, General Series UWRL/G 85/03, p. 000–000.

Kaliser, B. N., and Fleming, R. W., 1986, The 1983 Landslide Dam at Thistle, Utah: American Society of Civil Engineers Geotechnical Special Publication 3, p. 59–83.

Ozment, J., 1983a, The slide at Thistle; Denver, Rio Grande Western Railroad, Document JLO 042482, 7 p.

—— , 1983b, The Thistle, Utah landslide: Denver, Rio Grande Western Railroad, Document JL 00811283, 37 p. (Internal memo from J. Ozment to Denver & Rio Grande Western RR, September 1983, Exhibit A, *in* Court Records, The Denver & Rio Grande Western RR v. Utah Railway Company, U.S. District Court, Salt Lake City, Utah, Civil No. C83-1130J).

Peterson, R. P., 1952, Geology of the Thistle area Utah: Provo, Utah, Brigham Young University, 72 p.

Rawson, R. R., 1957, Geology of the Spanish Fork Peak quadrangle, Utah: Brigham Young University Research Studies, Geology Series, v. 4, no. 2, 33 p.

Rigby, J. K., 1962, Some geomorphic features of the southern Wasatch Mountains and adjacent areas: Brigham Young University Geology Studies, v. 9, part 1, p. 80–84.

—— , 1968, Guide to the geology and scenery of the Spanish Fork Canyon along U.S. Highways 50 and 6 through the southern Wasatch Mountains, Utah: Brigham Young University Geology Studies, v. 15, part 3, 31 p.

—— , 1976, Field guide, northern Colorado Plateau: Dubuque, Iowa, Kendall/ Hunt Publishing Company, 207 p.

Shroder, J. F., 1967, Landslides of Utah [Ph.D. thesis]: University of Utah, Salt Lake City, Utah, 27 p.

—— , 1971, Landslides of Utah: Salt Lake City, University of Utah, Utah Geological and Mineral Survey Bulletin 90, 51 p.

Terzaghi, K., 1950, Mechanisms of landslides, *in* Paige, S., chairman, Application of geology to engineering practice: Geological Society of America, Berkeley Volume, p. 83–123.

Witkind, I., and Page, W., 1983, Geologic map of the Thistle area, Utah County, Utah: Utah Geological and Mineral Survey Map 69, scale 1:24,000.

MANUSCRIPT ACCEPTED BY THE SOCIETY FEBRUARY 21, 1992

Geological Society of America
Reviews in Engineering Geology, Volume IX
1992

Chapter 10

Recent developments in landslide mitigation techniques

J. David Rogers
Rogers/Pacific, Inc., 396 Civic Drive, Pleasant Hill, California 94523

ABSTRACT

This chapter begins with a brief synopsis of landslide repair methodologies developed over the past 70 years. Early attempts at stabilizing slopes focused on emplacement of toe buttresses and inclusion of subdrainage. As earthwork equipment became larger and more capable, the removal and recompaction of entire slide masses became commonplace. Over the past decade, geotextile and geomembrane products have become available that can significantly alter the options for repair, especially under conditions of restricted access or poor weather. In the balance of the chapter, I seek to introduce the reader to some of these products and to case histories of ways in which they have been combined to effect novel solutions to slope stability problems.

INTRODUCTION

It has been more than 40 years since Karl Terzaghi's (1950) now-classic paper appeared in the Geological Society of America's *Applications of Geology to Engineering Practice*. In the interim, little has changed with respect to understanding the theorems of effective stress and progressive failure that promote slope instability.

Since 1950, increased development in hillside areas has underlined the importance of understanding the geologic factors promoting instability before beginning engineering analysis or repair. All too often, sites prone to landsliding have been the scene of repeated repair attempts within a few years of each other. Experience over the past half-century tends to suggest that many landslide repair attempts are made without benefit or full understanding of the geometry and hydrologic regimen of the affected sites. In addition, the blind implementation of a traditional, engineered repair scheme, for example, recompaction, may not serve to mitigate adequately all manner and form of future slope instability.

In this chapter I explore some of the more innovative techniques available for landslide repair that have come into practice in the past decade or so.

The rational design of a landslide repair cannot begin until the factors of site geology are properly evaluated. In most engineering analyses, the fundamental factors are: (1) the relative position of the ground-water table; (2) the fluctuation of ground-water levels and the flow volumes ascribable to infiltration or subaqueous flow aquifers); and (3) confirmation of the presence, character, and geometric extent of both ancient and active landslide slip surfaces.

Mitigation via excavation and recompaction

The earliest engineering attempts at landslide correction likely occurred along railroad and canal embankments in England and France, beginning in the 1830s. As the industrial revolution took root in the late nineteenth century, powered excavation machinery such as track-mounted steam-powered shovels spearheaded a revolution in earthwork construction. From 1850 to 1950, most cut slopes were excavated at slopes of 1:1 (45°) or steeper, and fill was placed on embankments of about 1.5:1 (horizontal to vertical). Steeper embankments were accommodated by stacking rock or masonry blocks to create gravity retaining walls, then filling at 1.5:1 above such structures.

When disaster struck in the form of a slope failure, the style or method of repair depended on cost and the available right of way (Sharpe, 1938). In rural areas, such as cut slopes on the Panana Canal (MacDonald, 1913, 1947), failed excavations were simply laid back to a more stable inclination (from 1:1 to 10:10 in some cases). In more urbanized or mountainous areas, where there was little available right of way, concrete and masonry gravity retaining walls were most often employed (Ladd, 1935).

Self-propelled earth-moving equipment began to show up on the civil engineering scene in the 1920s as part of the ambitious road-building programs being employed throughout the

Rogers, J. D., 1992, Recent developments in landslide mitigation techniques, *in* Slosson, J. E., Keene, A. G., and Johnson, J. A., eds., Landslides/Landslide Mitigation: Boulder, Colorado, Geological Society of America Reviews in Engineering Geology, v. IX.

United States. With self-propelled equipment, landslides could be excavated and replaced with some more suitable material, such as drain rock or riprap. By the 1930s, most large landslide repairs consisted of either partial excavation of the headscarp area and/or the placement of toe buttresses, most commonly over existing creeks or gullies (Terzaghi, 1931). Such repairs were usually effected in combination with some sort of subdrainage, either withdrawal wells or trench subdrains (Larkey, 1936; Root, 1938; Greeley, 1940). A scheme typical of this early era is shown in the upper half of Figure 1.

By the mid-1940s, sheepsfoot compactors began to be employed for so-called "dry" compaction of large earth embankments (for example, the Hansen Flood Control Basin) and rock-fill dams (the San Gabriel Dam). Up to this time (1942), only smooth tire compactors with contact pressures of about 40 psi had been available. The sheepsfoot roller allowed contact pressures of around 250 psi, a six-fold increase in compactive effort (Baumann, 1936, 1937, 1941; Proctor, 1933). In the years following World War II, large earthwork projects became com-

monplace with the introduction of larger, self-propelled hydraulic-powered equipment and the infusion of large projects spawned by the Interstate Highways Act of 1955 and water retention, reclamation, and flood-control projects, sponsored by the U.S. Bureau of Reclamation and the U.S. Army Corps of Engineers.

In constructing larger cuts and fills, some were invariably placed across ancient landslide deposits without benefit of geologic engineering input. By the late 1950s, a new style of repair came onto the scene, known by most practitioners as the "recompacted buttress fill," shown as the lower half of Figure 1.

Buttress fills remain the most commonly employed method of landslide repair in the United States. They are identical to new construction embankments in that they employ shear key benches, which are excavated beneath zones of disturbance (landslide slip surfaces) or potential distress, such as soil and organic horizons. In landslide repairs, subdrains are almost always included at the heels of the key benches in order to alleviate pore pressures that promote land slippage (Forbes, 1947).

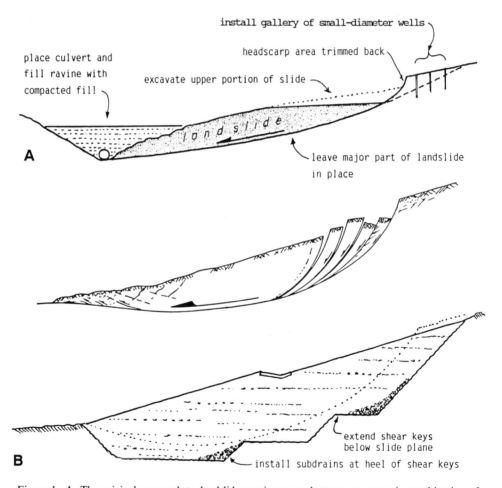

Figure 1. A, The original approach to landslide repair was to buttress toe areas in combination of limited removal of the upslope area, trimming back the headscarp and installing wells to draw down the watertable. B, As earth-moving equipment became more capable, the entire mass of a landslide could be excavated and recompacted in a buttress fill. Often such buttresses are constructed with subdrains composed of free-draining material.

Removal and replacement techniques have inherent liabilities. The landslide material must necessarily be excavated, carried, and stockpiled at an adjacent location. In large slides, it is possible to excavate in one area, simultaneously placing the excavated muck in another area already excavated and prepared for fill placement. However, in steep terrain, available stockpile area may be scant, requiring the construction of temporary fill-stockpile fences.

A second liability is the normally high moisture content of the slide material, which is usually excessive in the season following the earth movement. The slide material often requires scarification, drying, and/or mixing in order to bring moisture levels close to optimum for placement at 90% to 95% relative compaction. This requires additional handling, warm sunny days (or appreciable wind), and a larger working area.

Simple recompaction of low-strength materials can be dangerous in that compacting does not change the mineralogical makeup of the material. Soft, expansive clay will still be expansive, if not as soft. Even though compacted to a high degree of density, the fill is still able to absorb additional water through swelling or mineralogical absorption by cation exchange with percolating ground water. It is for these reasons (and subdrain clogging) that many recompacted buttress fills have failed over the past 35 years.

Conventional retention structures

A variety of retention structures have been successfully employed to repair land slippage where high-value structures are inextricably involved with the repair. The types of structures are basically divisible into four main categories: (1) gravity structures; (2) cantilever structures; (3) flexible and/or bulkhead walls; (4) retained structures; in addition, combination structures can incorporate one or more of the methods.

Examples of the traditionally employed wall structures and engineered retention systems are shown in Figures 2–6.

Landslide mitigation using subdrainage

Types of subdrains. Where differential settlement or grievous loss of property are not immediately apparent due to distance, landslides sensitive to pore-pressure buildup can be effectively mitigated by simply providing sufficient underdrainage (Root, 1938, 1955a; Forbes, 1947; Stanton, 1948; Cedargren, 1989).

Equipment sizes now permit the construction of large continuous trench subdrain systems that can be backfilled with geotextile or rock mixtures. Figure 7 shows a typical outline of the various types of subdrain applications in landslide repairs.

Pipes. The type and style of perforated pipe for conventional or trench subdrains need to be considered. The designer should consider overburden pressure, long-term maintenance, differential settlement potential, and corrosion resistance. Thick-wall ABS pipes are currently the most favored for cost, corrosion

resistance, and ability to be maintained by roto-rooter or rodding. ABS-Truss pipes are particularly strong and well suited for deep subdrain applications. Clean-outs for periodic maintenance are now standard at every turn or 500 ft (~150 m) of straight section, and 90° bends are typically not allowed. PVC, polyethylene, and polypropolyene all degrade under ultraviolet radiation. Polyethylene flex lines and crush lines have very low tolerance for earth loading and should never be utilized in underdrainage applications.

Cost considerations. In utilizing an approach wholly dependent upon subdrainage for landslide mitigation, several key factors will likely govern the cost: access for crawling excavator or backhoe; hauling distance of rock or gravel from the drop point; available topographic slope for drainage outlets; hauling away of spoils and waste; and availability of pervious granular backfill. Hauling of material from the drop point can be done with portable conveyers if conditions warrant. Drainage outlets (if topographic slope is insufficient) might be handled with large sump pumps or outletted via hydraugers drilled from sufficient distances downstream (Forbes, 1947; Herlinger and Stafford, 1952; Root, 1955b).

On the basis of cost only, the emplacement of subdrains alone would appear to be economic compared to other methods such as retaining structures or removal and replacement. An example of a subdrain-only repair is presented in Figure 8. A typical comparison of cost versus safety factor on a small repair is presented in Figure 9.

Most engineers are hesitant to use subdrainage alone, because there are no guarantees that the drains will continue to function for a long period of time without problems. These problems include clogging by dispersive clays, cohesionless silts, or the root systems of dense stands of vegetation. Rodents can make homes of subdrain outlet pipes, or these pipes can become overgrown near their discharge (or daylight) point, causing the system to back up. Hard ground water can deposit calcium carbonate around the percolation slits in subdrain pipes or well casings. Subdrains necessarily require maintenance or periodic replacement. As a consequence, most practitioners prefer to design with "defense-in-depth," using subdrainage in combination with other measures such as walls and recompacted buttresses.

Soil reinforcement using geomembranes and geosynthetics

Types of geosynthetics and geomembranes. Over the past decade a plethora of geosynthetic materials has become available for use as seepage membranes, pavement crack stoppers, tank liners, and soil reinforcements. These products are marketed in the following categories.

1. *Pavement cloths* are usually marketed as crack-stopper membranes such as Petromat; they are tack-coated as an overlay to existing pavement. Then a new surface of asphalt-concrete is placed upon the membrane. Crack-stopper membranes can be relatively impervious (woven fabrics) or pervious (spun fabric).

2. *Filter cloth* membranes such as Mirafi, Supac, and Tri-

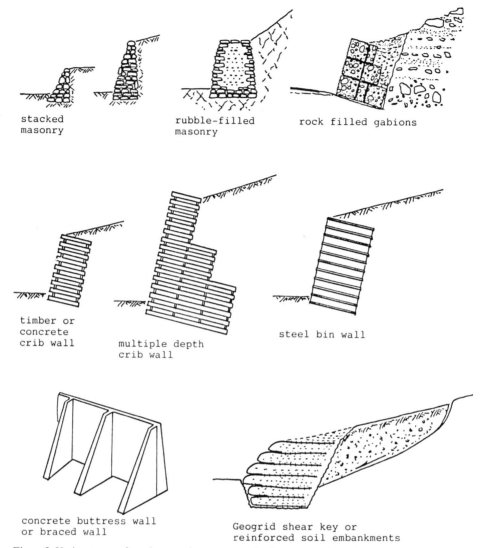

Figure 2. Various types of gravity retention structures. Such structures depend upon their sheer mass as a resisting force to the load imposed by a hillside. This is the earliest type of retention structure, having been used by Assyrians and Egyptians beginning around 2900 B.C.

vera are marketed mainly as seepage-filtration barriers. these are most commonly used beneath railroad ballast and highway aggregate base courses to prevent infiltration and settlement of the gravel into the underlying soils. Filter cloths can also be used to line subdrains constructed in drainage swales, hillsides, fill embankments, and areas prone to landslides or debris flows. Filter cloths are pervious, usually being composed of a spun, needle-punched cloth. These cloths can be lapped or sewn together in the field or at the factory.

3. *Liner membranes,* such as Hypalon, are designed as impervious membranes to effect cut off of contaminated ground water, "clean" ground water (for example, from swimming pools), or leachates from dump areas or embankments. Liner members are impervious, and are usually composed of rubbery compounds that can be sealed with the use of hand-applied solvents, so two sections of membrane can be joined together.

4. *Drainage membranes* are composites of the above materials; they necessarily combine some sort of seepage membrane with an attached filter cloth. Drainage membranes are beginning to be widely employed in the construction of retaining walls.

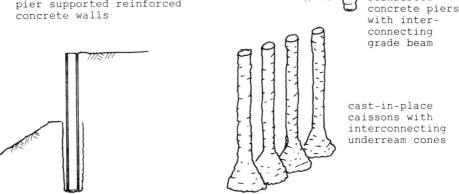

Masonry Block or Speed Block

reinforced concrete cantilever

inside stem wall

reverse stem wall

pier supported reinforced concrete walls

cast-in-place reinforced concrete piers with inter-connecting grade beam

cast-in-place caissons with interconnecting underream cones

steel H-pile wall

Figure 3. Various types of cantilever retention structures. Such structures came into use with the advent of pile driving, which dates back to Roman times. The use of large-diameter augers allows such structures to be constructed in stiff soils and soft rock.

These products include Enkamat and Enkadrain, Miradrain, Tensar DC-1200, and TENAX TN, TENAX MNT, and TENAX TNT.

5. *Soil reinforcement grids* include Geogrid products from Tensar, Nicolon, and Tenax. They are beginning to be widely employed in the construction of soil and rock embankments. The grids are of open-mesh construction, usually composed of polypropylene or polyethylene with carbon-black ultraviolet radiation inhibitors. The grids are constructed by mechanical pulling after roller extrusion. As a consequence, they typically possess anisotropic strength properties, one direction being stronger than the other. This stronger direction is typically aligned parallel to the fall line of the adjacent slope, to reinforce the soil most efficiently and resist downslope movement.

Corrosion resistance and expected longevity. The "laboratory" of engineering theory is experience. Because geotextiles are a recently introduced technology, the data relating to their actual use are only for about 10 years. However, experience to

J. D. Rogers

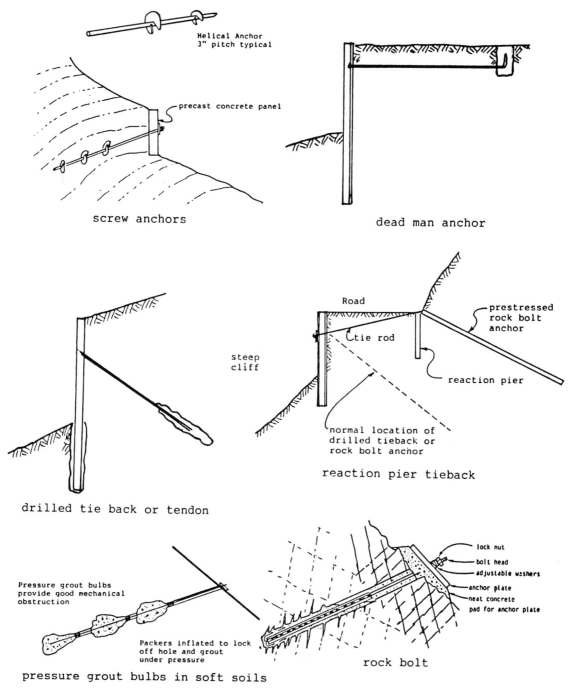

Helical Anchor
3" pitch typical

precast concrete panel

screw anchors

dead man anchor

Road

prestressed
rock bolt
anchor

tie rod

reaction pier

steep
cliff

normal location of
drilled tieback or
rock bolt anchor

reaction pier tieback

drilled tie back or tendon

Pressure grout bulbs
provide good mechanical
obstruction

lock nut
bolt head
adjustable washers
anchor plate
neat concrete
pad for anchor plate

Packers inflated to lock
off hole and grout
under pressure

rock bolt

pressure grout bulbs in soft soils

Figure 4. Various types of retained structures—those employing tension elements. The cost and feasibility of such structures is almost wholly dependent on drill rig access and drillability of the ground.

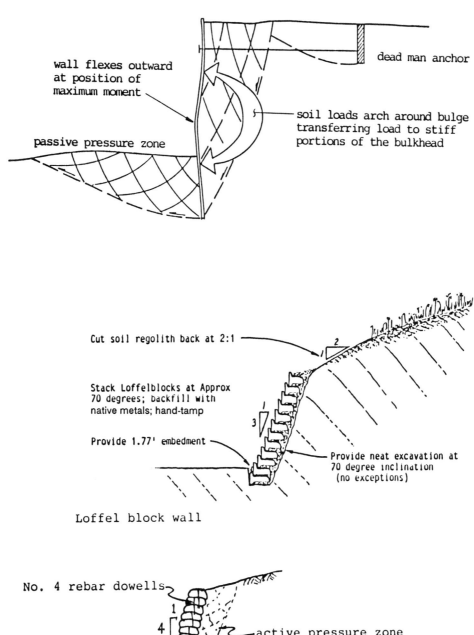

wall flexes outward
at position of
maximum moment

dead man anchor

soil loads arch around bulge
transferring load to stiff
portions of the bulkhead

passive pressure zone

Cut soil regolith back at 2:1

Stack Loffelblocks at Approx
70 degrees; backfill with
native metals; hand-tamp

Provide 1.77' embedment

Provide neat excavation at
70 degree inclination
(no exceptions)

Loffel block wall

No. 4 rebar dowells

toe embedment

active pressure zone
limited to 45-ø/2

sackrete wall

Figure 5. Various types of flexible retention structures, or those that deflect in order to shed their imposed loads. Such deflection lessens wall loads by allowing the ground mass to mobilize its shear strength (Rankine active pressure theory).

Loffelblock Structures

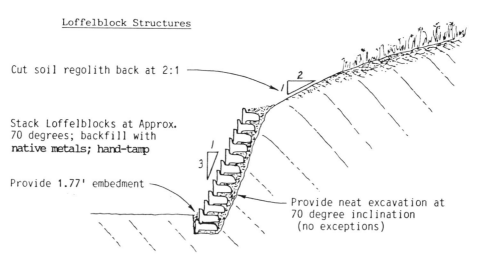

Cut soil regolith back at 2:1 ⎯

Stack Loffelblocks at Approx.
70 degrees; backfill with
native metals; hand-tamp

Provide 1.77' embedment ⎯

Provide neat excavation at
70 degree inclination
(no exceptions)

Figure 6. The Loffelstein, or Loffelblock retaining wall is a design concept emanating from Austria, and is now produced in the United States. Extremely economic, its primary application is for slopes under 22 ft (~6.6 m) high with an angle of internal friction, ϕ, greater than 30°. In the case shown, the wall was constructed on a 20% longitudinal gradient to support a highway cutslope. Such walls can be built for $12 to $15 per square foot (in 1988 U.S. dollars).

date with such materials has been very promising. Geogrids can melt when exposed to flames, but are not combustible.

Metalliferous Products. Engineers began using geotextiles to extend the expected lifetime of buried structures. In the 1950s and 1960s, metalliferous subdrain pipes, collectors, conduits, and culverts were buried in embankments as part of rationally designed civil engineering works. These included such products as perforated metal pipes (PMP), corrugated metal pipes (CMP), steel and aluminum culverts, and steel binwalls, iron pipe, threadbar reinforcing rods (tiebacks), steel H-piles, and galvanized metal reinforcing strips.

The presence of chlorides, in any dose, was found to be extremely detrimental to the longevity of buried metal elements. Salt, in any concentration, has an appreciably hard effect on buried metal objects. Steel or iron structures subject to high tensile stresses near water have been found to be susceptible to

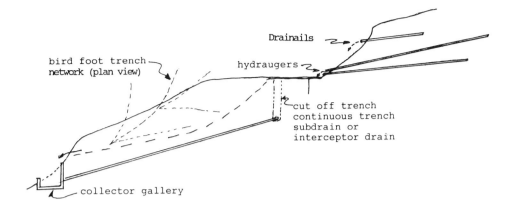

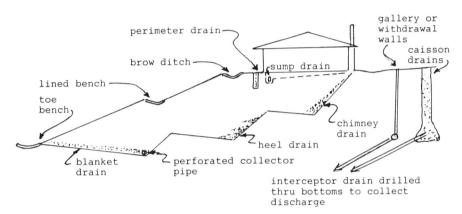

Figure 7. Traditionally employed nomenclature of the various types of subdrainage measures used by most geotechnical practitioners.

hydrogen embrittlement, a physiochemical process by which the steel structure is attacked and snaps under load, causing catastrophic failure. Mercury, in even the smallest concentrations, attacks aluminum with noticeable severity.

Over the past 30 years, the empirical relation between corrosivity and soil resistivity has been recognized and researched by the American Society of Testing and Materials, the Electric Power Research Institute, and other governmental agencies, such as state highway departments. These organizations have concluded that soil pH is a basic determinator of longevity and a cause of problems. Soil resistivity of less than 2000 ohm-cm usually indicates that some sort of corrosion protection is required, and resistivities of less than 500 ohm-cm indicate extremely high corrosivity, thereby negating the use of metals for long-term applications.

Plastics and Composites. In the late 1960s, products like polyvinyl chloride (PVC) pipe began to be utilized in some buried pipe–conduit–subdrain applications due to its light weight, high strength, and small cost. However, time has shown that plastics possess their own problems, including (1) long-term embrittlement due to absorption and/or exposure to hydrocarbons

and acid rain; (2) embrittlement due to ultraviolet radiation exposure; and (3) strength loss ascribable to long term creep under sustained loading.

As plastics were used more, new elements were marketed. These included the following.

Styrene plastic is lighter, more brittle, and subject to the same detractions as PVC, but cheaper.

Polyethylene pipes are impregnated with carbon-black to better resist ultraviolet deterioration, but are of insufficient strength to withstand any sort of sustained loading.

Acrylonitrile Butadiene Styrene (ABS) was introduced in the late 1970s to provide a high-strength plastic with built-in defenses for those environmental factors that caused problems for PVC. ABS possesses few reaction problems, even with corrosive fluids. It is not sensitive to ultraviolet radiation and is constructed with sufficient sidewall thickness to be sewer-standard and capable of withstanding rooter cleaning. Since 1984, ABS has also been available in truss construction, permitting the highest degree of bending resistance within a minimum weight section.

Polypropylene products such as geotextiles and some geogrid materials are the least suitable for long-term exposed applica-

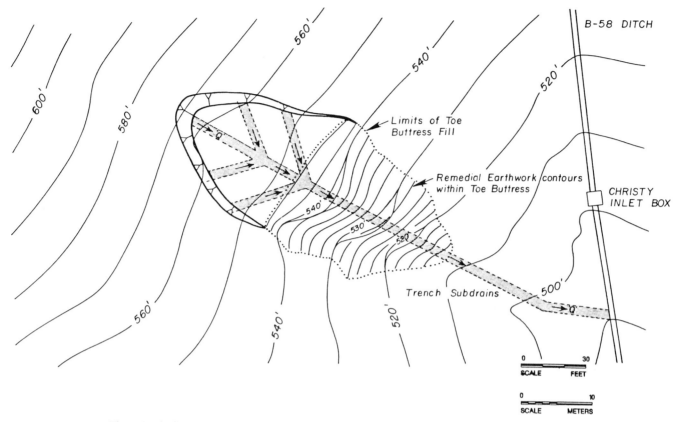

Figure 8. Birdfoot-style trench subdrain network, as seen in plan view. Simple trench subdrains offer a low-cost alternative for slide repairs in rural areas where subsequent ground movement due to consolidation and/or creep is of little consequence or economic concern.

tions because of their susceptibility to breakdown under ultraviolet radiation. Ultraviolet inhibitors such as carbon-black and protective coatings can be used, but they only serve to retard the breakdown process, not to prevent it. Ultraviolet breakdown is most acute in higher elevations (>5000 ft [~150 m]) where there is less filtration of the sun's ultraviolet rays.

Polyester products such as Trivera Spunbond or Bidim filter cloths are the most stable (and most expensive) product with regard to corrosion resistance and inherent resistance to ultraviolet radiation breakdown.

High-density polyethylene (HDPE) is utilized in a wide array of products, such as flex-wall pipes, Geogrids, Geoweb cells, impermeable membranes, and erosion-control mats. All of those products are impregnated with carbon-black to help retard ultraviolet breakdown.

Fiberglass–nylon–rayon roving fibers are beginning to be used in soil reinforcement. These can be of continuous strands (roving) or discontinuous strips. Fibers can be crimped or smooth. They are generally mixed with cohesionless granular fill materials such as sand and decomposed granite.

Applications. In the following pages, section views of various geosynthetics and slope facing elements are presented. The remaining figures present case histories of applications that I and others have used to mitigate slope instability.

Mechanically stabilized embankments

Beginning in the early 1960s, the French architect Henri Vidal proposed reinforcing beach sand with pine needles to increase its bearing capacity, and patented the idea of Reinforced Earth. The concept is similar in precept to what occurs naturally with tree roots (see Fig. 10). By providing some form of tensile reinforcement, the sand was engendered with some degree of cohesion, thereby enabling it to support greater loads., The reinforced Earth concept spread to the United States by 1969, when a 50-ft-high (~15 m) vertical Reinforced Earth® wall was constructed on California Route 39 near Islip Saddle in the Angeles National Forest.

Other Reinforced Earth, and VSL Corporation's competing Retained Earth, systems were utilized mostly on highways through the 1970s. The California and Georgia Departments of Transportation developed their own similar retention systems. In the early 1980s, Netlon Corporation of Great Britain introduced Tensar Geogrid, a high-density polyethylene (HDPE) grid im-

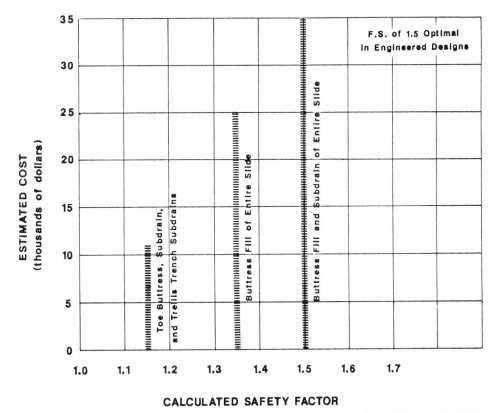

CALCULATED SAFETY FACTOR

Figure 9. Comparison of estimated cost versus safety factor for three styles of landslide repair (in 1984 U.S. dollars). In this case, the partial toe buttress and trench subdrain alternative cost the least, but also offered the lowest safety factor. If the consequences of future failure are not deemed to be excessive, trench subdrains can be very cost effective.

Figure 10. Nature's concept of soil reinforcement is shown to good effect in the root network of a banyan tree, here stabilizing a nearly vertical cut in colluvium on a National Park Service trail at Diamond Head, Oahu, Hawaii. Water percolating through the colluvium serves to propagate the expanding root system. The new technologies of micropiles, soil nailing, fiber-reinforced soil, and bioengineering emanate from this natural example. In terms of frictional contact area, such tropical trees are easily capable of engendering 10,000 psf increased shear strength to the soil.

pregnated with carbon-black. The grid is manufactured by heating and stretching thick perforated stock. Geogrids come in a variety of sizes, depending on the level of intended loading once buried in the ground. These soil-reinforcement grids work on the same principle as the Reinforced Earth and Retained Earth concepts; that of providing tensile reinforcement through frictional contact with the surrounding soil. The basic concept of entraining soil-reinforcement grids in landslide stabilization is presented in Figure 11.

Soil-reinforcing grids serve to increase the unit shear strength of any soil in which they are emplaced, thereby offering much higher long-term factors of safety than are possible through simple compaction. This is because no matter how intense the original compactive effort, soil density is eventually lessened through saturation, swell, and creep, factors that occur over many years. In situ soil reinforcement also allows the designer to vary the steepness of the slope's finished face, allowing vertical faces when necessary.

Soil reinforcement can also allow compaction activities to proceed through wet weather periods, when traditional levels of compactive effort are not achievable. In wintertime slide emergencies, saturated soils involved in sliding can be mucked out and

Erosion Control with Geosynthetics

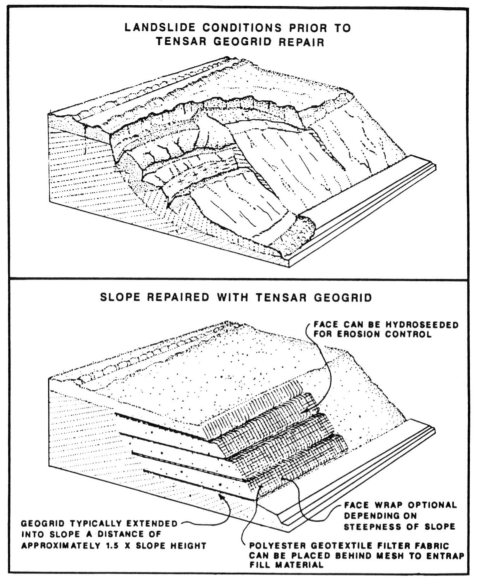

Figure 11. Schematic representation of the basic tenants of a Geogrid reinforcement repair scheme. A wide array of grid strengths is now available, as are competitive products manufactured by Tenax and Nicolon. Embedment lengths generally vary from 1 to 1.5 times the embankment height.

replaced with either drier soils or free-draining gravel as buttress fill material with benefit of the in situ soil reinforcement. With gravels, soil reinforcement allows steeper, conforming slopes to be constructed in the worst of environmental conditions.

Reinforcing grids are generally placed at lift separations of 2 to 4 ft (~0.6–1.2 m), as shown in Figure 12. Face wrapping of the grids is an option. The upper photo in Figure 12 shows a mechanically stabilized embankment under construction with a vertical face wrapping; the lower photo shows a slope under

construction with a flush inclined face wrapping. The term "mechanically stabilized embankment," or MSE, was originally coined by the California Department of Transportation to provide a generic name for all of the various proprietary systems. The Federal Highway Administration has since adopted that term to describe generically all in situ soil benefication retention systems. Some typical cross-sections of mechanically stabilized embankments are presented in Figure 13. The wide embankment portrayed in the upper half of Figure 13 is a landslide repair keyed

Figure 12. A, Placement of welded wire mesh soil reinforcement near the face of a vertical embankment structure during construction. Soil is then spread over the mesh and compacted in 6–8-in-thick (~15–20 cm) lifts. The area immediately adjacent to the free face usually requires local compaction with hand-operated vibratory equipment. B, Compaction of fill lifts in a landslide repair between successive layers of Tensar Geogrid with face warps at 4 ft (1.2 m) intervals. The slope face was repaired at a slope of 1.7:1 directly beneath a series of existing structures.

into underlying Cretaceous siltstone and shale. The lower half depicts a rock-cut repair in Miocene sandstone. Note how the length of embedment decreases with increasing slope inclination. This is because the normal force engendering friction to the grids is greater under a steeper slope due to increased overburden and the increased steepness of maximum principal stress trajectories. An additional factor governing calculation of required grip length is competency of the underlying materials. Leshchinsky and Bodeker (1989) described in greater detail how design judgment is incorporated into MSE designs.

In a weathered bedrock cut in fairly competent materials, the failure surface is generally shallow and more planar, often a wedge or slab-type failure. In such materials, weathering, relaxation and/or creep, and near-surface seepage pressures have likely precipitated the failure. Less-weathered bedrock materials generally lie a short distance beneath the failed material: there, the reinforced soil mass may be designed like a gravity retaining wall supporting very low lateral soil pressure (if adequate subdrainage is incorporated into the fill). If the structure possess insufficient capacity to resist sliding or overturning, additional tensile reinforcement of the underlying bedrock may prove both effective and economic.

Face wrapping with reinforcement grids generally provides an excellent mulch surface to resist rill erosion and promote planting. Figure 14 shows before and after photos of a face-wrapped slope taken only eight weeks apart during the winter rainy season. Face wrapping with the grid also helps retard rodent burrowing into the slope. Vegetation serves to protect the grids from ultraviolet degradation and vandalism. Because soil is exposed in grid mesh MSEs, volunteer vegetation will generally take hold on the slope regardless of initial landscaping efforts. In all cases, vegetative cover serves to provide an aesthetic surface which has the double benefit of reducing erosion.

Face wrapping the grids can also serve to create steeply inclined supporting structures such as toe buttresses and retaining walls, as shown in Figure 15. Toe buttress support capacity is greatly increased by the inclusion of reinforcement grids, because the embankment will act as a massive reinforced wall with built-in subdrainage. Face-wrapped embankments have special application to failed bedrock cut slopes, as presented in Figure 16 (the design section presented in the lower half of Fig. 13). Face wrapping is most effective in limiting subsequent erosion of the repaired slope, desired along highways and creek channels.

An alternative to face-wrapping grids is to place false layers of grid at 12 in (~30.5 cm) intervals adjacent to the embankment face (Fig. 17). These false layers usually extend only 3 to 5 ft (~0.9–1.5 m) into the embankment while conventional full-length grid layers are interspersed at 2 to 5 ft (~0.6–1.5 m) spacings. False layers effectively reduce the exposed slope height to 12 in (~30.5 cm) by providing a nonerodable, free-draining boundary that interrupts run-off velocity. Minor surface sloughage of the top few inches of the embankment is necessary to retard run-off–induced erosion. Vegetative cover then provides a sort of protective mat to retard raindrop spatter and provide a more tortuous path for overland flow. Although soil-reinforcing grids are not combustible, they can melt in brush or range fires. In such instances, exposed portions of the grid may melt, taking at the most a few inches of surface reinforcement off the slope. False layer or nonface wrap slopes can be constructed as steeply as 45° (1:1; horizontal to vertical) and are now the normal procedure for slopes of 1.5:1 or flatter inclination. Some representative exam-

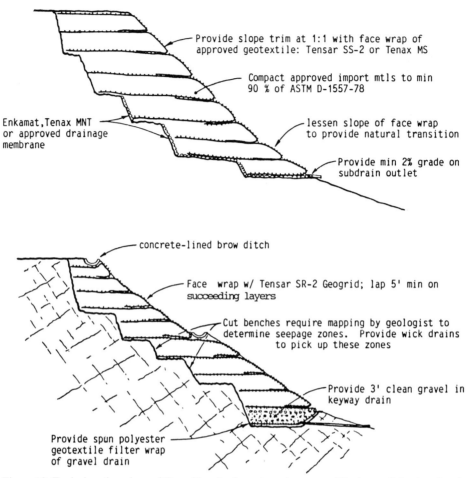

Figure 13. Typical section views of Geogrid embankment repairs accomplished on soil (top) and rock (bottom) slopes with inclinations of around 1.5:1. The employment of prefabricated drainage membranes at the heel of keyways helps to speed up jobs with steep grades and tight working areas.

ples of non-face wrap embankments are presented in Figures 18 and 19 (the slope shown in Fig. 19 suffered a brush fire four years after it was constructed).

Combination mechanically stabilized retention structures

As with every successful invention, a number of competing MSE systems are now available to the consumer: it is hoped that this competition will also promote some lowering of unit material prices. Soil-reinforcing grids can be mixed with any number of facing elements to provide a myriad of structure types and styles,

such as gabions, wire mesh, masonry blocks, gunite over geotextile fabric, and precast concrete panels.

Figure 20 presents an example of a rock-filled, gabion-faced, mechanically stabilized embankment. This style of combination structure seeks to combine the better attributes of each support system. Gabions are free draining and extremely flexible; their as-built shape is more nondeforming with time, they provide greater roughness at high flow (thereby keeping erosive scour velocities low), and they are noneroding. Their single drawback is in the cost of imported rockfill and the labor costs associated with rock placement within the gabion baskets. By emplacing a Geogrid-reinforced embankment behind the gabion facing, on-

Figure 15. A, As-built view of a Geogrid gravity retention structure constructed using native gravelly colluvium. Total wall height is ~10 ft (~3 m) with a grip distance of 10 ft. B, As-built view of a vertical Geogrid retention structure constructed on a 20% grade to support a roadway crossing of a colluvial-filled swale. Tensar SS-2 geogrid was utilized with crushed gravel at the outside face to act as a protection against fire, rodent activity, and to provide a reaction surface for compaction near the exposed face.

Figure 14. Two views of a Geogrid-reinforced landslide repair accomplished on an emergency basis between October and December 1986 in Crockett, California. The lower view shows the finished slope six weeks after completion in late January 1987. The slope had been hydroseeded and Geogrid face wrap acts as an excellent mulch mat.

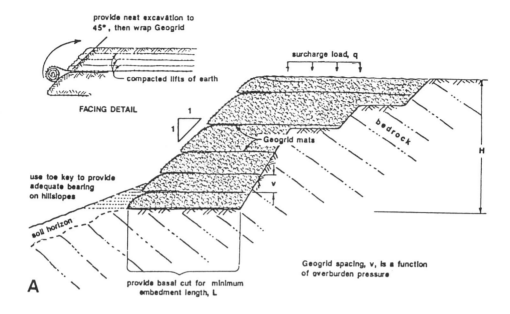

Figure 16. A, Typical face wrap detail on a Geogrid reinforced embankment steeper than 1:1. The grid provides an excellent mulch for hydroseeding, much like jute mesh. B, As-built view of a face-wrapped Geogrid repair on a 60-ft-high (~18 m) cut slope failure that involved bedrock exposed in an old 1:1 road cut. The repair of such steep slopes cannot be accomplished with traditional methods of removal and recompaction. Note excellent cover of hydroseeded grass.

site materials could then be utilized, handled, and compacted by labor-saving mechanical means.

In the late 1980s many small masonry block support systems became available in the United States. The more common of these include Keystone, Earthstone, and Loffelblock. Some representative examples of the Loffelblock type are presented in Figure 21. These interlocking blocks are basically intended to support clayey slopes of less than 5 to 6 ft (~1.5–1.8 m) high or bedrock cut slopes up to 22 ft (~6 m) high. The block systems are generally designed utilizing a 1:4 to 1:3 backward batter to reduce

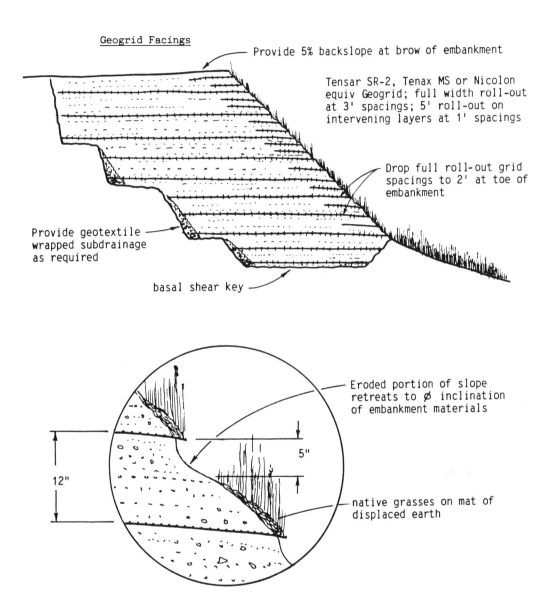

Geogrid Facings

— Provide 5% backslope at brow of embankment

Tensar SR-2, Tenax MS or Nicolon equiv Geogrid; full width roll-out at 3' spacings; 5' roll-out on intervening layers at 1' spacings

— Drop full roll-out grid spacings to 2' at toe of embankment

Provide geotextile wrapped subdrainage as required

basal shear key —

— Eroded portion of slope retreats to ⌀ inclination of embankment materials

5"

12"

— native grasses on mat of displaced earth

Detail view of the erosion which can be expected to occur between Geogrid layers. The effective slope height is reduced to 12" by embedment of the Geogrid.

Figure 17. As an alternative to face wrapping, intervening layers of Geogrid can be placed at the slope face to create effective slope heights on the order of 1 ft (~0.3 m).

Figure 18. Two views of a 1:1 Geogrid-reinforced fill embankment constructed without benefit of face wrapping, but with short-face grid layers spaced at 12 in (~30.5 cm). The lower view shows the effects of hydroseeding several months later.

Figure 19. Two views of a 1:1 Geogrid-reinforced roadway embankment with short-face grid layers spaced at 12 in (~30.5 cm). Note the natural blending of the fill with the surrounding slopes, an aesthetic feature of soil-reinforced structures.

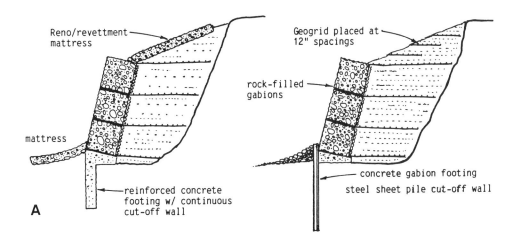

Figure 20. A, Schematic section view of gabion-faced Geogrid embankments constructed as part of a bank repair along Alhambra Creek in Martinez, California. The use of soil backfill lessened off-haul costs for excavation and negated two-thirds of the required rock fill import necessary to fill a conventional all-gabion retention structure. B, Photograph of the completed channel repair, looking downstream. Wall height is 9 to 12 ft (~2.7–3.6 m) with a 6-ft-deep (~1.8 m) footing to protect against undercutting.

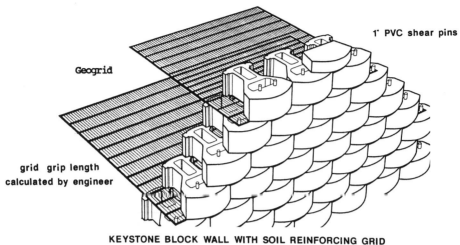

KEYSTONE BLOCK WALL WITH SOIL REINFORCING GRID

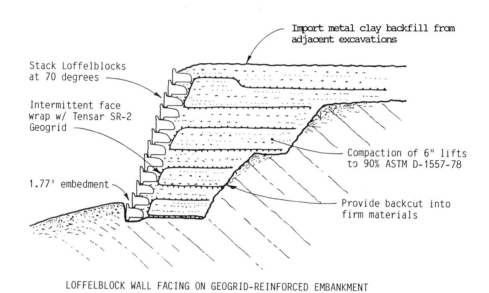

LOFFELBLOCK WALL FACING ON GEOGRID-REINFORCED EMBANKMENT

Figure 21. Schematic views of Loffelblock and Keystone combination block with Geogrids.

active earth pressures acting on the blocks. Because of their thin width (generally under 24 in [~61 cm]), the resultant thrust of such walls can easily be drawn outside the middle third of the wall's footing. As a consequence, these walls are usually constructed with a reinforced concrete footing, having the basal course of blocks wet set in the concrete at the proper batter. By themselves, these blocks are most effective in facing fairly competent bedrock cut slopes (materials with an angle of internal friction greater than 35°).

Keystone makes use of 1 in (2.54 cm) diameter PVC shear dowels between the blocks, which can also be utilized to attach soil grid–reinforcement mats, similar to the example presented in

Figure 21. The precast block is utilized as a facing element for the geogrid-reinforced embankment. It must be remembered that in mixing these products, they have very dissimilar stiffnesses. The reinforced soil must strain some noticeable amount to develop shear strength along the Geogrid-soil interfaces. If the abutting wall facing is not constructed with sufficient flexibility, individual blocks may crack in shear as the soil they are restraining flexes outward.

In the early 1980s, Hilfiker Corporation of Eureka, California, introduced the welded wire mesh wall, or Hilfixer mechanically stabilized embankment support system. Examples of this system are presented in Figure 22. Like gabions, this system can

Figure 22. A, Earthen lift being spread over welded wire mesh. In lifts about 2 ft (~0.6 m) high, a mechanically stabilized highway embankment with vertical face was constructed across an active landslide area. B, As-built view of a welded wire mesh embankment constructed parallel to the road's 10% grade. The face may deform outward as the fill consolidated with time, especially when wetted.

Figure 23. A, Construction view showing emplacement of welded wire mesh facing elements being used with Geogrid soil reinforcement to construct a 0.5:1 embankment slope below a proposed office complex. Welded wire mesh retention systems have been promoted for some years by Hilfiker Corporation in California and Pacific Wire in Tacoma, Washington. Such systems are employed by the same theories applicable to Geogrids and geomembranes. However, Geogrids can be less expensive to purchase and place because they do not require extensive tying. B, As-built view of the completed embankment of 11,000 yd³ (~8360 m³) beneath the Crest Office Park complex, Martinez, California.

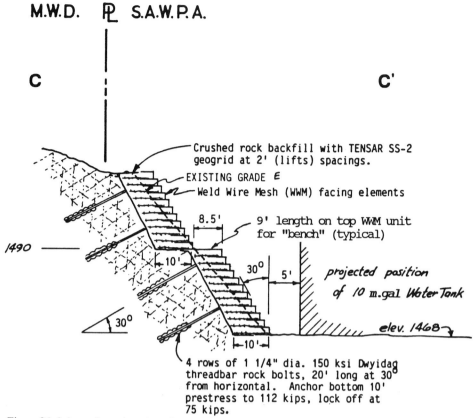

Figure 24. Schematic section view of a combination structure employed to repair a 60-ft-high (~18 m) cut slope failure in granite. The original cut slope was made at 0.5:1, greatly limiting repair measures. A neat excavation was made into the repair area by using presplit drill lines with conventional burden blasting. The burden was then mucked and crushed to a –6 in size. With 2 × 4 ft (~6 × 1.2 m) bent-L welded wire sections, a gravity structure was concurrently constructed from two starting levels, one at the slope base, the other at mid-height. Crushed rock was placed behind the wire facing and reinforced at 2 ft (~6 m) intervals with Geogrid. At four levels, prestressed rock bolts 20 ft (~6 m) long on 20 ft centers were installed to reinforce the broken rock face and reduce the required wall width from 25 ft (~7.5 m) down to 9 ft (~2.7 m) (by tying the active pressure zone into compression). The repair was effected in the winter: rainfall had no effect on rock compaction or excavation activities. The project was located at Lake Matthews, near Riverside, California.

be utilized as a facing element for soil grid–reinforcement products. Wire-mesh facing possesses a number of favorable attributes: being very light, a lot of product can be shipped to a job on a single truck and easily handled; it is basically fireproof and corrosion resistant (if the FHWA 2 oz ft[2] galvinizing specification is maintained), the mesh sets up easily, and, by stipulating offsets between lifts (commonly 2 ft [~0.6 m]; see upper half of Fig. 22A), any slope inclination desired can be easily constructed. Wire-mesh facing looks neat when finished and is extremely easy to landscape. An example project is presented in Figure 23.

Wire mesh–faced walls can also be utilized in steep, inaccessible terrain, as shown in Figure 24. In this case, a 70-ft-high (~21 m) rock slope cut at 0.5:1 in granodiorite had begun to undergo a toppling failure. Very little access room was available to effect a repair, and a property line existed just above the crown

of the cut. A neat excavation was made into the repair area by utilizing presplit drill lines with light, outward burden blasts. The burden was then mucked and crushed on site to –6 in (~15.25 cm) size. Using 2 × 4 ft (~0.6 × 1.2 m) bent-L sections of welded wire mesh (see Fig. 25), gravity structures were concurrently constructed from two levels; one at the slope base, the other at mid-height (working down from the top). Crushed rock was placed behind the wire facing and reinforced at 2 ft (~0.6 m) intervals with geogrid. At four levels prestressed rockbolts 20 ft (~6 m) long on ~20 ft centers were installed to reinforce the exposed rock face and reduce the required wall width from 25 ft (~7.5 m) down to 9 ft (~2.7 m) (by tying the active pressure zone into compression). The repair could have been effected in winter months, because rainfall would have no effect on compaction of previous rock backfill.

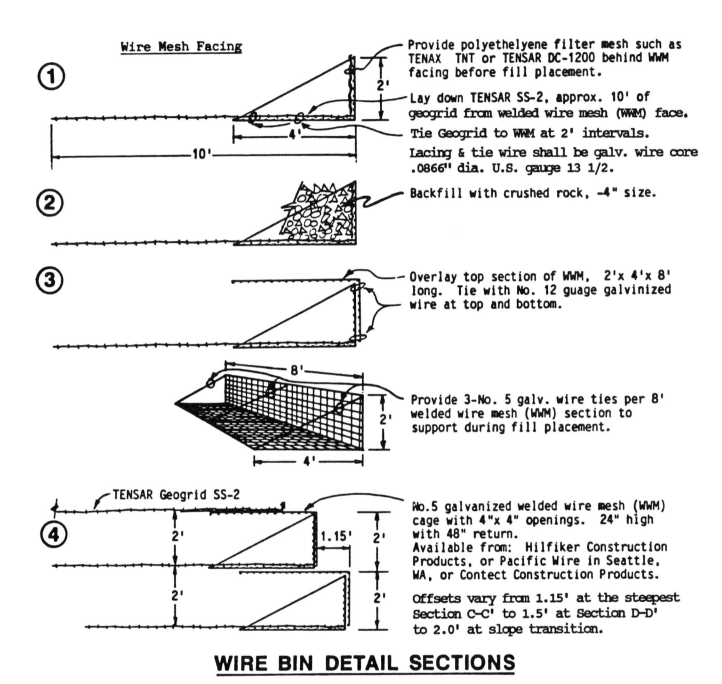

Wire Mesh Facing

① Provide polyethelyene filter mesh such as TENAX TNT or TENSAR DC-1200 behind WWM facing before fill placement.

Lay down TENSAR SS-2, approx. 10' of geogrid from welded wire mesh (WWM) face.

Tie Geogrid to WWM at 2' intervals.

Lacing & tie wire shall be galv. wire core .0866" dia. U.S. gauge 13 1/2.

② Backfill with crushed rock, -4" size.

③ Overlay top section of WWM, 2'x 4'x 8' long. Tie with No. 12 guage galvinized wire at top and bottom.

Provide 3-No. 5 galv. wire ties per 8' welded wire mesh (WWM) section to support during fill placement.

④ TENSAR Geogrid SS-2

No.5 galvanized welded wire mesh (WWM) cage with 4"x 4" openings. 24" high with 48" return.
Available from: Hilfiker Construction Products, or Pacific Wire in Seattle, WA, or Contect Construction Products.

Offsets vary from 1.15' at the steepest Section C-C' to 1.5' at Section D-D' to 2.0' at slope transition.

WIRE BIN DETAIL SECTIONS

Figure 25. Placement details for utilizing welded wire mesh as facing elements for Geogrid-reinforced embankments or retention structures. In mountainous areas, the welded wire mesh has the advantage of being fireproof over the Geogrid (which won't burn, but will melt). The 2 × 4 ft (~0.6 × 1.2 m) welded wire L-sections are widely available in the western United States. A single or double overlay, as shown here, can be used. Prefabricated filter mats or polyester filter cloths can be employed behind the mesh to inhibit piping. Polypropalene filter cloth products are not employable because they degrade quickly under ultraviolet radiation.

118   *J. D. Rogers*

REFERENCES CITED

Baumann, P., 1936, Wear on sheepsfoot rollers: Engineering News Record, June 11, 1936, v. 116, p. 835–836.
—— , 1937, Wear on sheepsfoot rollers decreased by revised design: Engineering News Record, May 13, 1937, v. 118, p. 707–708.
—— , 1941, Design and construction of San Gabriel Dam No. 1: American Society of Civil Engineers, Proceedings, v. 67, no. 7, p. 1199–1238.
Cedargren, H. R., 1989, Seepage, drainage and flow nets (third edition): New York, John Wiley & Sons, p. 292–336.
Forbes, H., 1947, Landslide investigation and correction: American Society of Civil Engineers Transactions, v. 112, p. 377–442.
Greeley, D. H., 1940, Prevention of slides as a safety factor: California Highways and Public Works, v. 19, no. 5, p. 13–15.
Herlinger, E. W., and Stafford, G., 1952, Orinda slide: California Highways and Public Works, v. 31, no. 1-2, p. 45–60.
Lackey, J. M., 1936, New method of soil stabilization, a feature of the Coast Highway Project: California Highways and Public Works, v. 15, no. 3, p. 22–23.
Ladd, G. E., 1935, Landslides, subsidence and rockfalls: Proceedings of the 36th Annual Convention of the American Railway Engineering Association, Chicago, v. 36, p. 1091–1163.
Leshchinsky, D., and Boedeker, R. H., 1989, Geosynthetic reinforced soil structures: Geotechnical Engineering Division American Society of Civil Engineers Journal, v. 115, no. 10, p. 1459–1478.

McDonald, D. F., 1913, Excavation deformations: 12th International Geological Congress, 12th, Ottawa, Canada, Transactions, p. 779–792.
—— , 1947, Panama Canal slides, *in* The Panama Canal, the Third Locks Project: Balboa Heights, Canal Zone, Department of Operations and Maintenance, Panama Canal Commission, 73 p.
Proctor, R. R., 1933, Fundamental principles of soil compaction: Engineering News Record, v. 111, no. 9, p. 245–248.
Root, A. W., 1938, Problem of slipouts studied by state highway engineers: California Highways and Public Works, v. 17, no. 3, p. 18–19.
—— , 1955a, Horizontal drill: California Highways and Public Works, v. 34, no. 3-4, p. 26–29.
—— , 1955b, Correction of landslides and slipouts: American Society of Civil Engineers Transactions, v. 120, p. 281–289.
Sharpe, C. F., 1938, Landslides and related phenomena: New York, Columbia University Press, 171 p.
Stanton, T. E., 1948, Hydrauger method: California Highways and Public Works, v. 27, no. 1-2, p. 6–10.
Terzaghi, K., 1931, Earth slips and subsidence from underground erosion: Engineering News Record, v. 109, p. 90–93.
—— , 1950, Mechanism of landslides, *in* Berkey, C., ed., Applications of geology to engineering practice (Berkey Volume): New York, Geological Society of America, p. 83–123.

MANUSCRIPT ACCEPTED BY THE SOCIETY FEBRUARY 21, 1992

Index

[Italic page numbers indicate major references]

Abalone Cove landslide, California, 2, *69*
Adenostoma fasciculatum, 20
Altamira Canyon, California, 71
Altamira drainage basin, California, 70, 76, 77, 79
Altamira Shale Member, Monterey Formation, 70
anorthosite, 2
aquifers, 95
Arctostraphylos glandulosa, 20

basalt, 71, 79
Bel Air, California, rainfall, 12
Benedict Canyon, California, 14
bentonite, 70
Beverly Hills, California, 14
Big Rock Mesa landslide, Malibu, California, 2, 3, 5
block sliding, 49
Bluebird Canyon landslide, Laguna Beach, California, 2
buttress fill, 96

caliche, 38
Carbon Canyon landslide, Malibu, California, 2
Ceanothus leucodermis, 20
chamise, 20
chaparral, 11, 20
chlorite, 80
chockstones, 7
Christmasberry, 20
clay, 7, 72, 78
claystone, 38
coastal landslides, 3
Cold Creek Member, 56
Colton Formation, 84
compound landslides, *1*
Conejo Volcanics, 56
conglomerate, 38, 84
construction performance, *30*
Contra Costa County, California, 24, 25
Crystal Lake, San Gabriel Mountains, California, rainfall, 11

debris floods, 11
debris flows, 1, 2, 11, 14, 83, 84
debris slides, 11
deformation, 2
dewatering, 70, 81
dewatering wells, 73, 78, 82
Diablo, Contra Costa County, California, 25
distress, landslide-related, 29, *32*
dolomite, 78
dolostone, 71
Douglas Fir, 20
drag faulting, 3

earthflow, 56, 62
Easton v. *Strassburger* case, *25*
Eastwood manzanita, 20
erosion, 3
evapotranspiration, 79
excavation, 95

fault zone, 64
faults, drag-related, 3
Flagstaff Formation, 84
flooding, 83
flow barriers, development, *7*
flow paths, development, *7*
fracture permeability, development, *7*
fractures, in landslides, 7

Garapito Creek, California, 56, 58, 62
glass, 71
Glendora, California, 20
gouge development, 7
grabens, 2
grading, 65
grading codes, *17*
grains, comminution, 7
grains, detrital, 7
Grapevine landslides, Transverse Range, California, 2
ground water, 6, *69*, 73, 88, 95

Hansen Flood Control Basin, California, 96
hazard potential, *1*, 47
headscarps, 2, 56
hematite, 73
Hidden Springs, San Gabriel Mountains, California, 14
horizontal drains, in landslide mitigation, *63*
hydrocarbon, generation, 7
hydrodynamic flow, 7
hydrostatic pressure, as contributing factor, 63

insurance, 29
Interstate Highways Act of 1955, 96
iron, 80
iron oxide, 73, 78
iron sulfide, 73
irrigation, 8
Islip Saddle, Angeles National Forest, 104

Juana Diaz Formation, 38, 47

Keys v. *Romley* case, *23*

La Crescenta, California, 12
Laguna Beach, California, 2
Lake Elsinore, California, 17
limestone, 38, 84
Long Beach Harbor, 69

Los Angeles (City of), California, *63*
grading codes, 18
slope failure potential, 21
storm damage, 12
Los Angeles Coastal Plain, 69
Los Angeles County, California, 24, 69
storm damage, 12
grading codes, 17
Los Angeles Harbor, 69

magnesium, 80
Malibu, California, 2, 5, 24
Mameyes, Puerto Rico, landslide (1985), *37*
manganese oxide, 78
Martinez Formation, 64
McAllen Ranch gas field, southern Texas, 7
Middle Fork of Mill Creek, California, 14
mitigation, *63*, 90, *95*
monitoring, importance of, 35, 36
monitoring wells, 73
Monterey Formation, 69, 70
Monterey Park, California, 17
Mt. Wilson, California, rainfall, 11, 12
mudflows, 83
mudstones, 2

Navajo Sandstone, 85
nitrate, 80
North Horn Formation, 84

oaks, 20
olistoliths, 4
Orange County, California, grading codes, 17
Pacific Palisades area, California, *63*
Palos Verdes Peninsula, California, 2, *69*
Panama Canal, 95
Pasadena, California, rainfall, 12
perched water tables, 1, 8
percolation, 76, 77, 78, 81
Photinia arbutifolio, 20
pinnate drag faults, 7
Ponce, Puerto Rico, 37
Portuguese Bend landslide, Palos Verdes Peninsula, California, 2, 3, 69, 71
Portuguese Point, California, 71
Portuguese Tuff, 71
pyrite, 73

Quercus dumosa, 20

rain water, infiltration, 6
rainfall
excessive, 37

related to ground water, 73, 76
related to slope failure, 6, 7, *11*, 85
Rambla Pacifico landslide, Malibu, California, 2, 5
"reasonable care" concept, *23*
recompaction, 95
remedial treatment, *35*
retention structures, 97
Riverside County, California, 17
root reinforcement, 20
Rosita gas field reservoir, 5
Rubio Canyon, California, 12

sagebrush, 84
Salt Lake Valley, Utah, 83
San Ciriaco Hurricane (1899), 37
San Dimas Experimental Forest, California, 20
San Gabriel Dam, California, 96
San Gabriel Mountains, California, rainfall, 11, 12
San Jacinto, California, 17
San Jacinto River, California, 17
San Juan Capistrano, California, 2
San Juan Creek landslide complex, San Juan Capistrano, California, 2
San Pedro Hill, California, 69
sandstone, 5, 38, 56, 84, 107
Santa Monica Mountains, California, 6, 56

rainfall, 12, 19
scarp
head, 2, 56
landslide, 38, 43, 47
scrub oak, 20, 84
secondary landslides, *1*
seepage, 84, 88
septic waste water disposal, 6, 7, 8
sewage, 56, 59, 77
shale, 14, 56, 71, 78, 84, 107
shears, 47, 64
Shields Canyon, California, 12
siltstone, 56, 64, 71, 78, 107
slope failure
hillside, *11*
Pacific Palisades, California, *65*
slope instability, 33
slope stability analysis, *51*, 67
smectite, 71
snow melt, 85
sodium, 80
sodium montmorillonite, 71
soil reinforcement, 105
South Hallettsville gas field reservoir, 5
Spanish Fork Canyon, Utah, 83
Spanish Fork Creek, Utah, 83
Spanish Fork River, Utah, 84, 88
Sprecher v. *Adamson* case, *24*
stabilization, 36

standard penetration test (SPT) blow counts, 47
Stone Canyon, California, 15
strain, 4
subdrainage, 97
sulfate, 80
surface water law, *23*

Terzaghi effect, 6
Texas, southern, 7
Thistle landslide, Utah (1983), *83*
Topanga Canyon, California, 17
landslide (1978), *55*
rainfall, 12
Topanga Formation, 56
Transverse Range, California, 2
tropical storm Isabel, 37
tuff, 71

Utah, 11

volcanic breccia, 56

Walnut Creek, Contra Costa County, California, 24
Wasatch Front, Utah, 83
water table, 52, 72, 73
watersheds, burned, 12, 21

Zachau Canyon, California, 12